AUTHOR'S NOTE

We live in a day when the art of deception has been finely honed. From television commercials, to social media platforms, to a culture permeated with New Age and political doublespeak, our children are bombarded with half-truths, high-tech gimmicks, and outright lies. And if these sophisticated seductions are not enough, the traditional enemies of our young people--pride, peer pressure and the need for acceptance--are standing in the wings to further complicate and endanger their lives.

The *Century War* books are expressly written to help our young people learn to discern these and other centuries-long spiritual conflicts that have shaped our nation, past and present. One of the writing techniques we employ to aid the development of critical thinking skills is the use of multiple points of view.

A City of Lies has three points of view: two protagonists (the heroes) and the antagonist (the villain). By allowing the reader to experience the story through the eyes of opposing main characters, the reader can explore the characters' motivations, thoughts, and reactions. In doing so, the reader learns to distinguish truth from deception, and, along with the story's characters, struggles with the difficult issues that obscure the path to adulthood.

These three points of view are interwoven with the drama of a fictional 19th century utopian community, the false hopes of progress, and the dark dawn of the criminal underworld in Chicago. We hope that students, parents and teachers alike will take time to ponder the many lessons that can be gleaned from this pivotal point in America's social and spiritual history.

YOUNG HEROES

A CITY OF LIES

John L. Jenkins
Mark W. Weaver

CHRISTINE THOMPSON and ADAM VESTRY are Providentially reunited four years following their first adventure in The Invisible Empire. The year is 1876. Chicago, just five years after the Great Fire, continues to rebuild its reputation as Queen of the West. The nation stands on the threshold of greatness, and a hope in Progress reigns.

Christine, determined to make her own way, joins a beautiful utopian community called New Eden, where new ideas, hard work and equality have seemingly recreated Paradise. Adam, now an investigative magazine reporter, pursues connections between organized crime and business. Adam discovers that beneath Chicago's gemlike surface lies a dark and dangerous underworld where greed and power bring ruin to all who dare embrace it.

Adam follows a trail of corruption to the doorstep of New Eden. He will need all his wits and his faith to rescue Christine and to foil the evil that seeks to bring flames and destruction to the Queen of the West once again!

Century War, Book 3

STORYSHOPUSA.COM
MANASSAS, VIRGINIA

A City Of Lies
John Jenkins, Mark Weaver

storyshopusa.com

ISBN: 978-1-940072-17-3

Published by Story Shop USA, Manassas, Virginia 20110.

Cover design: Story Shop USA
Front cover and interior drawings: Steven Philip Morales
New Eden Map: Mark Weaver

Library of Congress Control Number: TBD

A CITY OF LIES

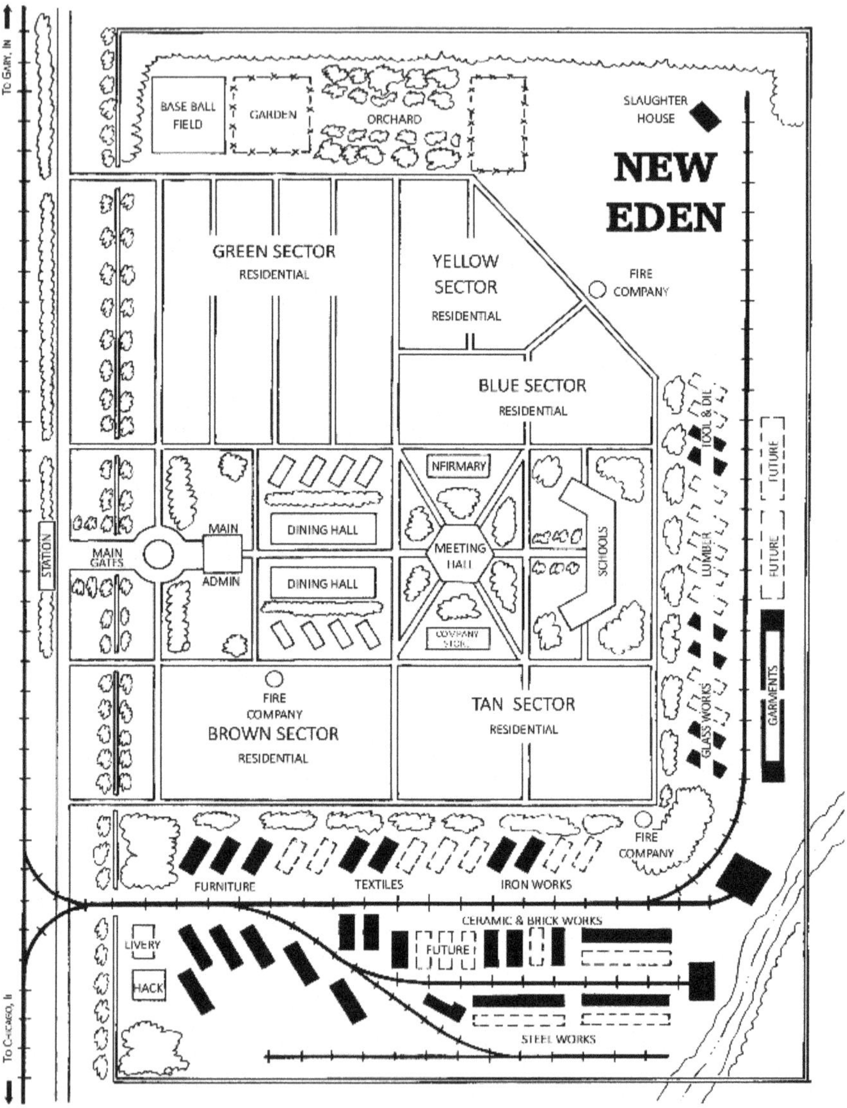

NEW EDEN
To Gary, In
To Chicago, Il
STATION
MAIN GATES
MAIN
ADMIN
BASE BALL FIELD
GARDEN
ORCHARD
SLAUGHTER HOUSE
GREEN SECTOR
RESIDENTIAL
YELLOW SECTOR
RESIDENTIAL
FIRE COMPANY
BLUE SECTOR
RESIDENTIAL
NFIRMARY
DINING HALL
DINING HALL
MEETING HALL
COMPANY STORE
SCHOOLS
TOOL & DIE
LUMBER
GLASS WORKS
FUTURE
FUTURE
GARMENTS
FIRE COMPANY
BROWN SECTOR
RESIDENTIAL
TAN SECTOR
RESIDENTIAL
FIRE COMPANY
FURNITURE
TEXTILES
IRON WORKS
LIVERY
HACK
CERAMIC & BRICK WORKS
FUTURE
STEEL WORKS

CHAPTER 1
PENNSYLVANIA DAY

OVER the western bank of the Schuylkill River, near the Philadelphia city line, sprawled the city of the future. Over two hundred buildings and brightly colored pavilions covered 285 acres, celebrating the first 100 years of American growth. On this bright September holiday in 1876, railroads, streetcars and steamboats rushed as many as 22,000 visitors to the Centennial Exposition every hour.

Three fashionably dressed young women stood beneath a flagpole in front of the Main Exhibition Hall. Above them a white flag with the word PROGRESS in red letters fluttered lightly in the breeze.

"I've never seen so many people in one place," Christine Thompson whispered as she took a seat on a long white bench facing the Main Exhibition Hall. Greta plopped down to her left and Amelia scooted in from her right.

Christine adjusted her straw hat. "I read that over the last five months, nearly eight million visitors have swarmed the Exposition. Folks from every state and dignitaries from around the world."

The afternoon sun lit her strawberry blond hair as it cascaded over her shoulders. She wore a burgundy cape over her white dress.

"What a wonderful surprise," Christine said with a smile, "bringing me here for my birthday. I can't thank you both enough."

"The tickets cost 50 cents each and I had to beg papa for the money. But it's your twenty-first birthday," Greta beamed. She twirled her red, white and blue silk parasol. "When I turn twenty-one, I hope my friends will do something equally nice for me!"

Amelia cupped her hand over her mouth and giggled.

Greta looked over quizzically. "What?"

Amelia adjusted the red bow on the front of her yellow dress, then tossed her braided black hair off her shoulders. "Yes, of course, we're here to celebrate Christine's birthday."

Greta stopped her parasol and shot Amelia a withering glare.

Christine sighed. Obviously, Greta and Amelia shared a secret, a secret Christine was not privy to, but could guess: boys.

But rather than let their silliness ruin her day, she turned her attention to the tremendous building in front of her.

She had also read that the Main Hall covered twenty-one acres under one roof. Dozens of flags high atop the mammoth structure rippled in the light breeze. Long rows of horse-drawn carriages packed with visitors of all ages rolled by on the wide avenue. Everyone was wide-eyed and open-mouthed, admiring the sights and crowds.

Greta smiled smugly. "It's an entire mile from one end to the other. This is my fifth visit and I still haven't seen it all." She snapped her parasol closed.

Christine peered up from under the straw rim of her hat at the flag.

The nation was changing so quickly, standing on the threshold of true greatness. Christine could not help but wonder where the nation would find itself in another hundred years. How far would America's ideals of freedom progress? And what role would women play?

For a moment, Christine smiled. She thought back to early that morning when she had wandered through Machinery Hall and had used something called a typewriter. For fifty cents of her own money, she had pressed small, round metal buttons called keys that transferred inked letters to a piece of paper. Included in the fifty cents was the price of an envelope and stamp, which she used to mail her letter to her best friend, Angelina MacDonald, who now lived in Gettysburg with her husband.

Greta snickered, pointing across the avenue. "There goes Abigail Johnston. Look at her old hoop skirt—she's so out of style!"

Christine pressed her lips tightly together. Young women like Greta and Amelia had a lot of growing up to do if they ever wanted to have an important role in the nation's glorious future!

Christine bolted erect as something sharp poked her ribs. She spun to find Greta withdrawing the tip of her parasol.

"I think I see James coming our way," Greta whispered.

With a mischievous grin, a young man strode toward them. He wore a tan top hat, a brown waistcoat, and fancy striped trousers.

"Good afternoon!" James bowed and removed his hat in one smooth motion.

Greta stepped forward. "This is Christine, the daughter of Reverend Thompson, pastor of the Second Methodist Church. Today is her twenty-first birthday. And you know Amelia."

Amelia's milky white face suddenly turned a rosy red.

James grinned and pointed at the flag. "And what a fine place to meet, Greta. I could see the flag all the way from the entrance."

Greta smiled and batted her eyelashes.

Christine suppressed a grin. She had been correct. All along, Greta had planned to meet James, using the birthday as a ruse.

"Can you believe this place?" James asked with a broad sweep of his arms. Then, with a deft movement of his hand, he flipped his hat onto his head and tapped it into place. "And I've never seen so many bicycles. I'll have to ask Father to buy me one."

"A two-seater, I hope!" Greta said, popping open her parasol and narrowly missing Christine.

"All it takes is a warm day and the exhibits feel like an oven!"

explained James. "Have you tried the Ice Water Fountain?"

"Yes, but I'll go again. These concrete paths feel like lava beneath my feet," Greta pouted.

As Christine watched Greta walk arm in arm with James, memories came rushing in of a young man who, four years ago, had offered Christine his arm. But Adam Vestry didn't care about fancy hats and flashy moves like James. And Adam worked hard for everything he owned. He was resourceful and determined to do what was right, even if doing right cost him his reputation. But Adam had left Philadelphia to start a new life in New York City four years ago, just before Angelina had married and moved to Gettysburg. In fact, all of her true friends had left Philadelphia.

Christine drew a deep breath. She would not let the circumstances of life get the better of her! This exposition proved that the future brimmed with limitless opportunities.

After quenching their thirst and enduring Greta's giggles at the Ice Water Fountain, Christine and Amelia followed James and Greta to the lake and stood beside the 35-foot-tall, copper-plated arm, hand and torch of the Statue of Liberty. Eventually, all of the pieces would be joined together on a small island in view of New York City.

But of all the inventions they saw that afternoon, the one that most captured Greta and Amelia's fancy was a device called the telephone. With a telephone, two people in different places could actually talk to each other over a wire.

Christine stopped beneath a tall pole supporting a gigantic, white-faced clock with gold-plated hands nearly six feet long. She wished her life and friendships would progress as fast as the nation. Amelia was too shy and immature. Eighteen-year-old Greta acted even younger. And when they were together—well, sometimes Christine could hardly bear it.

As the giant hands above Christine's head struck the five o'clock hour, James and Greta were nowhere in sight. A weary

Christine pulled Amelia aside.

"I'm going to find a bench at the front entrance and wait for your parents."

"I'll come, too," chirped Amelia.

As they approached the main gate, the smell of fresh breads, roasted meats and sausages, onions, and a mix of spices wafted stronger. Vendors crowded the wide avenue just outside the gates, and long lines of thirsty visitors snaked through the crowds to the soda fountains both inside and outside the gate.

Amelia's parents were already waiting for them. Mrs. Berger stepped quickly out of her carriage.

"Where's Greta?"

"She'll be along . . . eventually," Christine replied as she noticed the concern edging Mrs. Berger's eyes and mouth.

Amelia's mother placed a trembling hand on Christine's shoulder.

"We've got to get you home, right now. Your father collapsed at his desk after lunch and he won't come to."

CHAPTER 2

LEAVING TOWN

MEANWHILE, the wind gusting down the streets of New York was unseasonably cold. Suitcase in each hand, a young man with light brown hair jumped from the sidewalk into a waiting trolley.

After paying the driver, Adam Vestry set the suitcases on the wooden floorboards by his feet but remained standing near the door of the crowded car.

The driver urged his four-horse team into a trot.

The young man brushed a curl of hair off his forehead, tugged at the lapels of his wool jacket, and then stared out the front window. Steam-driven ships, barges and tugs crowded the New York City harbor and docks. Rarely did he see one of the old, but swift clipper ships with their wide, wind-filled scoops of white sail. He wished he had taken the time to book an ocean voyage, even if only a short one.

The driver noticed the young man's bags. "Leavin' town?"

"Yes, I am," the young man said with a huge sigh. "It's been a fine four years and I'll miss the Atlantic. I don't think I've failed to look at the ocean a single day."

The trolley lurched to a halt, pitching Adam forward against the front rail. Several passengers gasped with surprise.

The driver shook his head angrily.

A teenager in shabby clothes darted across the street, one hand pressing his cap to his head and the other held close to his chest, clutching a woman's purse. The ruffian pushed a heavily bundled woman, knocking both her and her two small children to the sidewalk. Then he leapt over a pallet of flour outside a baker's shop and burst down a trash-strewn alley.

The driver growled. "Not a single copper in sight. He'll never be caught."

"Neither he nor his gang," Adam remarked as he watched the boy clamber up and over a wooden fence at the end of the alley. "That's one thing I surely won't miss. Young toughs are everywhere these days. And they're getting younger and tougher."

"Don't even talk about Lower East Side," the driver grunted. "Hardly a night goes by without someone getting murdered."

As the trolley lurched forward again, the morning sun edged out from behind a bank of gray clouds. A change of color and brightness came sweeping across the harbor. The ocean sparkled as the tips of the waves caught the sunlight.

A faint smile stole over Adam's face as he drew a deep breath. The morning winds had taken the regular build-up of smoke and stench with it, at least temporarily. And temporarily was all that mattered, now.

"I've seen that happy look before," the driver chuckled. "Leavin' to meet a special lady or a new job? Which is it?"

The young man tore his eyes from the whitecaps to grin at the driver. His voice was suddenly thoughtful.

"I had a very special lady, once. She was my best friend. But that was four years ago. But you're right about a new job. That's why I'm leaving. I'll be working for a national news magazine.

"First, I have a five-week assignment in Washington, D.C. Since we're celebrating our nation's centennial, my magazine wants me to write a feature about America's first 100 years. I'll visit the White House and the Capitol, and meet with President Grant and Congress. I'm even scheduled to talk to one old-timer who was born in 1787—the year the Constitution was signed! Of course, I'll dig around for a few other unusual or interesting stories. Then I'm off to Chicago."

"Chicago?" muttered the driver, shaking his head. He snapped the reins. "That windy ol' city O'Leary's cow burnt down? Must be a mighty fine job you're headin' off to."

The young man smiled broadly at last.

Chicago was known for more than just the Great Fire back in '71. To the businessman and traveler, Chicago was known as Queen of the West, for its railroads, river and lake access. To the gamblers, corrupt politicians, and crime bosses whom Adam would soon be investigating, Chicago was the Gem of the Prairie, for its hundreds of roulette wheels, dicing tables and illegal deals.

But to a fearless investigative reporter, Chicago was simply a gold mine of opportunity!

Adam glanced at the driver. "Mighty fine job, it is."

Beneath clear blue skies, a slight breeze rustled the long stand of sugar maple trees bordering the cemetery southeast of Philadelphia. Sunlight danced on the bright yellows and fiery reds of the dying leaves.

Her father's simple wooden casket sat beside the open grave. Christine, dressed in black, stood between Mr. and Mrs. Abernathy, members of the Second Methodist Church of Philadelphia. Reverend Lokey, the pastor from First Methodist on the other side of town, began his eulogy.

Crowding the cemetery grounds were over a hundred friends and parishioners who came to pay their respects to the Reverend Matthew Thompson. Nearly half the guests were freedmen, blacks whom Matthew had helped during his 30 years of ministry.

Matthew's best friend, Sam MacDonald, stood on the opposite side of the casket. Sam's blue eyes were moist. The breeze had ruffled his silver hair. Christine remembered her father's friendship with Sam began in 1839 at the University of Pennsylvania. She thought of stories about how her father and Sam sat in the front row and listened to the heated abolition speeches by Dr. Theodore Weld and the Grimke sisters. Sam and her father had never been idle listeners, but always doers of the Word.

Christine watched Reverend Lokey close his black book. A squeeze on her left elbow from Myra Abernathy interrupted her musings. "It's your turn."

Christine gripped her Bible, stepped to the casket, and gathered her thoughts. She took a deep breath and began, hoping tears would not come until she had finished the eulogy.

"You all knew my father well. He gave his life to improve Philadelphia and help its people. I trust that you are as thankful for his many accomplishments as I am, perhaps most thankful for his work with the Underground Railroad in the years prior to the Civil War. Some of you standing here today escaped slavery because of his belief in freedom for all. But he was more than a civic leader and pastor; he was a deeply caring father."

Christine mustered her strength, her hands tightening around her Bible. She had rehearsed for this moment, over and over again. She paused and quietly cleared her throat.

"My father did not fear what men would think, caring only what God thought. During the years of the Underground Railroad, he often risked his life for what he believed. Both he and Sam MacDonald, whom many of you here know so well."

Christine paused and met Sam's gaze. "Both men sought to find a brighter future, and not just for themselves. They were not just men of words, but men of action."

Christine wavered, then grew strong again, blinking back tears.

"And that's the greatest praise I can give my father. I thank you for coming. And God bless you all."

Christine stepped away from the casket and returned to her

place between the Abernathy's. A chorus of "Amens" and "Hallelujahs" rippled around her.

Reverend Lokey folded his hands in front of him and began to sing Be Still My Soul. Everyone joined in as the pallbearers moved toward the casket. The ends of the four ropes were gathered up and the casket was slowly lowered into the ground.

Christine stepped to the edge of the grave. She threw autumn flowers onto the top of the casket.

"God speed your way home, Father," she whispered, wiping her eyes with her small handkerchief.

"God speed your way home!"

Two and a half weeks had passed since the funeral. Christine placed her last skirt in the suitcase. She closed the latch, then lowered it to the floor at the end of her bed. As she crossed the room, she paused to look at herself in the mirror above the dresser.

Her strawberry blond hair was tied up neatly. A slight bit of color in her freckled cheeks highlighted her bright eyes. From the attention numerous men had paid her after the funeral, she knew she had grown into an attractive young woman, no longer her father's little girl.

She sat on the bed and glanced at two opened letters. Aunt Mildred, who lived in a small town in western Pennsylvania, had written one, and her spinster Aunt Agnes, in Chicago, had written the other.

Christine bit softly at her lower lip. A number of church friends had encouraged her to stay in Philadelphia. Without a mother during her growing-up years, Christine learned to be independent and resourceful. She managed her father's house and his busy church schedule—no easy task! She planned teas, socials, luncheons and dinners. Life had often been one routine after another.

She folded the letters and slid each one back into its envelope. But stay in Philadelphia she could not. Just as the nation progressed, Christine knew she needed a season of change, of growth. To do so, she would have to leave Philadelphia, just as her best friends had done, to pursue their own lives and their own adventures. She would make new friends, though finding someone like Angelina would not be easy. Finding a special friend like Adam would be even harder.

Her father had not owned much, but she had sold the few possessions they owned: two horses, a carriage, and a few pieces of furniture. Several families had given her gifts of cash. After settling, Christine discovered that she had collected more than enough to make the trip and start with a modest reserve.

Now, she had only one decision left to make.

Sitting down on her bed, Christine thought about the letter of invitation from her father's older sister in Chicago.

Aunt Agnes had always been a wealthy woman, affording herself at least one maid and a gardener. As far as Christine knew, Aunt Agnes had never done any chores. All her money had come from a family inheritance. Christine's father had received his portion too, but he used it to help finance the Underground Railroad. Aunt Agnes disapproved and never let him forget it.

But perhaps now her aunt had put the past behind her. Aunt Agnes' letter seemed genuinely warm.

"Chicago brims with opportunity!" her letter read. "In the five years following the Great Fire, Chicago has been gloriously rebuilt. An industrious young woman can make a way for herself. Plenty of smart, well-to-do young men abound here, too."

Christine did not care much about the well-to-do young men part of the letter. In just the last two weeks, she had turned down four marriage proposals.

Suddenly, her lips curled upward into a soft smile. She placed the envelopes on the bed beside her and then, at some unknown prompting, offered a short, silent prayer for Adam Vestry and hoped the very best for him. Then, humming one of her father's favorite hymns, she stood up.

Her plans were set. She would leave on the evening train, travel all night, and arrive in the morning at her Aunt Mildred's in Paradise, Pennsylvania. There she would visit her cousin Melody for two weeks. Thankfully, Melody had agreed to accompany her to Chicago and stay for several weeks before returning to Paradise.

Christine faced the dresser. She lifted her chin and stared straight into the mirror. She had survived the loss of her mother fourteen years ago. She would survive the loss of her father.

Life and progress moved steadily, purposefully on.

And so would she.

CHAPTER 3
A SHORT STOPOVER

A steam whistle sounded a long, low wail as the train entered the Paradise city limits. Steam shot out in an expanding cone from beneath the train's squealing wheels.

Jarring sounds awakened Christine. Bolting straight up in her seat and rubbing her eyes, she realized that she had slept the entire night without waking.

Staring out the window, she watched as the train approached the trestle bridge crossing Vicar's Creek. Just before the bridge, she noticed a cracked and washed-out white sign with "Paradise" barely readable in faded purple and gold. Obviously, the sign needed replacing or, at least, a fresh coat of paint.

She remembered the last time she'd come to Paradise. Three years ago, their doctor encouraged her father to get away from Philadelphia for a few months to relax from the many demands of his pastorate. He and Christine traveled these very tracks and spent the spring with his sister-in-law Mildred and her daughter Melody.

The train rumbled over the old bridge and slowed as it neared the station. Following the contour of the creek, Christine eyed rows of small, wooden shanties and young children playing in a dirt road. Smoke curled upward from flimsy chimneys of rusted metal. Unsightly lines of laundry sagged between houses. The drab clothes almost touched the bare ground, capturing clouds of dust stirred up by playing children and the passing train.

Christine frowned as she propped her elbows on the windowsill and rested her chin in her palm.

She watched as the conductor leaned out over the railing and cried, "This stop, Paradise!"

Paradise? She had not remembered it looking so run-down.

The train pulled into the station. With faster bursts of steam, it screeched to a stop beside a one-story, brick station with a long wooden platform covered by a green tin roof.

Christine stood, adjusted the waistband of her floor-length brown skirt and tugged at the sleeves of her white, high-necked cotton blouse. She reached for her valise, let several people pass, and then entered the aisle by the door. She descended the metal stairs. A porter helped her to the platform.

"Christine! Christine! Over here!"

Turning to her right, Christine saw a young woman with a broad smile and oval face waving her arms and running down the platform. Her dark brown hair flowed loosely around her head and onto the shoulders of her simple, flowered dress.

"Melody, it's so good to see you! How you've grown! I can't believe you're already seventeen."

"You've changed, too," Melody replied, her eyes taking in Christine's finery. Then her smile faded. "I'm so sorry about Uncle Matthew. Now neither of us has a father."

Christine thought for a moment about Melody's father, John, who had died in the War. He had been killed by cannon fire at Gettysburg during the battle of Big Round Top. His casket had returned mostly empty, greatly increasing the family's grief.

The porter delivered Christine's suitcases.

Then, arm in arm, she and Melody strolled to her carriage. The porter followed with her bags.

"Where are your mother and your brother Matthew?" Christine asked.

"They're back at the house. Matthew's been pretty sick for a week now." The edge in Melody's voice concerned Christine.

"Normally, he's the terror of Paradise! A couple of weeks ago he got caught skinny-dipping with two of his friends in West Split Creek, just below the old mines!

"Well, you can imagine Mother's embarrassment! But now this sickness has him flat on his back. In bed. Luckily, the doctor says it's not contagious."

Christine waited for the porter to put her suitcases in the carriage, handed him two pennies, then climbed in next to her cousin. Melody snapped the reins, and the carriage jerked into motion down the dusty road.

Five minutes later, a sense of relief settled over Christine as the carriage rumbled across the bridge that spanned the creek. Crumbling old houses and long stretches of bare ground gave way to rolling grass-covered rises and woodlands.

Melody's house sat perched on a small hill overlooking the west side of town, facing steep hills punctured by a dozen of Paradise's old mines. The mottled gray-brown patchwork of rotting timber pilings that stuck out of the hillside and the rust-stained boards nailed over the entrances was an eye-sore.

At least Melody and her family lived away from the squalor by the tracks.

Aunt Mildred greeted Christine with a big hug and a kiss on the cheek. "We're so glad you could come, though the occasion is sorrowful. I sure wish we could've attended the funeral, but we know the pain you're going through."

Christine smiled. She had always liked Aunt Mildred. Aunt Agnes never seemed to care much for children or young people.

"Come sit in the parlor, Christine. Tell us about your trip."

The house was modest but comfortable. Compared to many of her friends' homes in Philadelphia, her aunt possessed little. Her matching pieces of brocade furniture were fading. She kept her wooden floors swept clean, but the braid rug in the middle of the room had frayed edges. And though Christine had never seen a better oil painting of George Washington, the gold paint on the frame had flaked off in several places.

But the piping hot tea and the small, freshly baked cakes Aunt Mildred served were just as good as Christine remembered.

After they had finished their tea and Christine her story, Aunt Mildred gave details of how Matthew had suddenly taken ill and now needed constant attention. The doctor still wasn't sure what had made Matthew so weak.

"If his condition persists, I'm afraid that Melody will not be able to go with you to Chicago," explained her aunt. Her voice trembled slightly. "I hope you understand."

Melody sat motionless on the other end of the sofa, her hands folded in her lap, her eyes downcast.

Christine nodded silently. She breathed slowly and tried hard not to show her disappointment. Her aunt had enough worries of her own.

"Of course, Aunt Mildred." Christine straightened her shoulders. "Don't fret even one minute. I'll be perfectly fine."

"You could stay here with us for a while," Melody offered with a weak smile.

"Agnes would understand, Christine. Your aunt knows you're closer to us." Aunt Mildred's eyes almost pleaded as she spoke.

"But I've already accepted her offer. Besides, I need a fresh start. I want to get on with my life."

Christine knew that was a half-truth. This was not the Paradise she was looking for.

An awkward silence stole over the room. Christine could hear the tick of the small anniversary clock on the mantle.

"What are you going to do in Chicago?" Melody finally asked.

"I'm not sure, but Aunt Agnes believes I will have numerous opportunities."

Aunt Mildred set her tea cup in its saucer, paused momentarily, then leaned toward Christine. "I don't want to create a rift, but we've always enjoyed having you here. Paradise is not a bad place to meet someone and raise a family. And there's talk about reopening the mines. Maybe this town will yet fulfill its destiny. Then Paradise will be bustling once again. You'll see."

Christine stared down into her empty cup. She wondered if her aunt genuinely believed what she was saying. More than once, Christine had heard her father say that the old mines had brought the people of Paradise only trouble and disappointment.

"I'll stay for two weeks, just as we planned," Christine said at last. "But then I'll be on my way."

A short while later, in her room, Christine unpacked the things she would need for her short stay, then sat down in front of the dresser table. She removed her hat and unpinned her hair.

Who are you, Christine Thompson? What do you really want to do with your life?

Doubt crept into Christine. She twirled her hair around her finger: Paradise or Chicago?

She wondered how her father might advise her, if he were alive. He always encouraged her to think for herself, to be independent.

Then she thought about her visit to the Centennial Exposition a few weeks earlier. In her mind's eye, she saw the white flag emblazoned with the word PROGRESS in red letters.

"No! There's nothing in Paradise for me!" she said out loud, walking away from the mirror. "I'm going to Chicago."

Adam Vestry closed his notebook, then looked up at the Washington Monument, a 150-foot squared-off stub of fancy, white Maryland marble framed by a sunny, autumn blue sky. Adam shook his head and sighed. The nation's monument to George Washington was still nothing more than a nesting place for birds and an occasional soggy home and rooting place for stray pigs.

The rustle of wings nearby preceded the swirling, upward flight of a dozen starlings. Darting left, then right, the dark-feathered birds wound their way up and over the monument, then out above the swamps and the slow-moving Potomac River.

Finally, Adam hoped, now that the Washington Monument Society had donated the monument to the federal government, this sad tribute to the nation's greatest hero could be completed.

He could hardly believe that the monument had been left derelict like this for 25 years.

If the Centennial Exposition in Philadelphia could take donations to help complete the 150-foot-tall Statue of Liberty designed by some Frenchman, then why wouldn't Americans be willing to help finish building the monument?

Adam feared he knew the answer: Progress, with a capital P. Most people, from the factory worker to the railroad baron, seemed more interested in what the future would bring for them than what they could learn from their past. And, when the future promised to pad their wallets and increase their bank accounts, no one invested in anything else!

His forehead lined with concern, Adam turned and tromped back through the swampy grounds toward Constitution Avenue. Maybe his article about the monument would help fuel public interest in seeing it completed.

And completing this article meant that his assignment in Washington was nearly over.

Adam could hardly wait to leave. Only two more weeks at Shepherd's Boardinghouse. Kindly old Mrs. Shepherd served great food and kept nice rooms. But Adam tired of the endless political arguments at the dinner table, and most of all, of having to look at George Washington's ugly, unfinished monument every day!

Just two more weeks. Then he was finally off to Chicago.

Chicago. Adam knew that his next assignment was going to be

far more difficult, and dangerous, than writing an article about the nation's first 100 years. But he would just have to wait until he got to Chicago and read the briefing paper from his boss that would be there waiting for him. Every new assignment began with a briefing paper, a report with background information to help him get started with his next series of feature articles.

Yes, he thought happily to himself, his next assignment would likely involve covert meetings with unsavory but interesting characters, stealth and spying, and a lot of hard legwork. Yes, indeed, it would be good to get back into the thick of things.

Adam smiled, ignoring the mud and muck that clung to his boots with every step.

November 2nd arrived and it was time to leave. Melody drove Christine to the Paradise station. Aunt Mildred stayed home with Matthew who was just beginning to recover. His sickness had been traced to poisons leaking down into the creek from the old mines.

They crossed the creek on the old stone bridge where the faded town sign stood in tall weeds. The shanties looked even dirtier than when Christine had passed them two weeks earlier. The children still played in the dirt road, kicking up small clouds of dust.

"I'll miss you!" Melody said through tears as they arrived at the train station. "If things don't work out with Aunt Agnes, you're always welcome here."

"I'll miss you, too, Melody. I'm sure I'll be back to visit."

Then the train whistle erupted with its last call for boarding. The conductor bellowed, "All aboard!"

The two hugged one last time. Then Melody reached behind the carriage seat and pulled out a package wrapped in newspaper and tied with string.

"Remember to return this to Aunt Agnes. She sent it to Mother months ago. I think it's a journal about the history of Paradise. All

I know is that Mother didn't like it very much."

The tall package would not fit in her valise, so Christine slipped it under her arm.

A porter pulled Christine's trunk from the carriage. "Miss, the train's about to leave. Better get on board."

Christine ran to the metal steps, valise in one hand, the package in the other. When she reached the top of the steps, she turned and waved goodbye one last time.

The whistle blew twice, one short, one long. Then, with the ever-quickening churn of mighty pistons and blasts of billowing white steam, the train pulled away from Paradise.

CHAPTER 4
STRANGERS ON A TRAIN

CHRISTINE approached the white-haired conductor. "Excuse me sir, I have a ticket, but I can't find a seat. Can you help me?"

The bored expression on the conductor's wrinkled face remained unchanged. He led her through to the next car. He pointed to an empty aisle seat near the middle of the car. The man sharing the bench seat wore an expensive wool suit, but an open newspaper blocked Christine's view of his face.

"There're more seats in the next car, if you don't like this one, Miss."

"I'm fine." Christine sat down without looking at the man beside her. She placed the valise and the package under her seat, adjusted her hat, and tried to make herself feel at ease.

She thought about Philadelphia and Paradise. An odd feeling crept over her with every passing mile the train sped down the tracks. No more church friends. No more Amelia or Greta, as silly as they were. No Aunt Mildred. No Melody.

Instead, she sat on a train beside someone she didn't know, on her way to a city she'd never visited, to live with an aunt she wasn't even sure she liked.

She fought off the wave of sadness by picturing the Centennial Exposition in her mind, and focusing on the white flag with the word PROGRESS in bright red. Yes, this trip was her journey into progress.

She set her lips determinedly, then adjusted her hat again. She had to face her fears straight on and overcome any doubts that tried to fight their way in.

The man sitting beside her closed his newspaper and folded it across his lap. Out of the corner of her eye, Christine could barely see the outline of his face. The silhouette of the nose, mouth and chin looked so familiar, reminding her of a face she had last seen four years ago. Reminding her of Adam Vestry.

Her father had challenged her to trust that God would guide her way. Could the man sitting beside her be—

She turned her head toward the man at the same moment he turned his head toward her. Their eyes met.

A stranger!

Christine blushed and looked away. How foolish of her to hope or think that God could arrange a chance meeting with Adam Vestry!

Folding her hands in her lap, Christine kept her eyes trained on the seat in front of her and waited in discomfort as the rush of blood to her cheeks slowly faded away.

After several embarrassing minutes, the man introduced himself. He was a Virginia state senator and a most gracious gentleman, on his way from Richmond to San Francisco.

The afternoon passed quickly.

At a stop in Ohio, Christine awoke from a brief nap and realized just how hungry she was. Looking out the window at the setting sun, she realized the senator had slipped out. After checking her hair in a small mirror, she left her seat and made her way to the dining car.

She quickly surveyed the arrangement of small, white cloth-covered tables lining either side of the car. She noticed several empty seats. Five rows down, she spotted the senator, his back to her. The chair opposite him was empty.

Christine smiled and walked down the aisle. She stopped beside his table just as he turned his head to glance out the window.

He swung his head around and looked up.

Christine's mouth fell open. She didn't even think to raise her hand to cover it.

Adam Vestry jumped to his feet, bumping the table. His glass of water teetered, almost spilling.

"Christine! I can't believe it's you!" His eyes sparkled.

"Adam? What—what are you doing here?"

"I should ask you the same question," he replied with a wide smile, motioning her to the chair opposite him. "Please join me."

A mixture of emotions flooded Christine as she slowly lowered herself in the chair. She studied Adam's lean face and warm eyes. His sandy hair and short sideburns had not changed at all. A small lock of hair still curled down his forehead.

"Choose anything you want from the menu," he said as a waiter approached the table. "Potato soup. Pork with dressing. Cod with mushrooms. Really, anything."

"Are you sure you can afford this?" Christine asked.

"I'll put it on my expense account," he replied, brushing the curl of hair from his forehead.

Christine tried to study the menu. She could hear the clickety-clack of the steel wheels rolling over the track and diners engaged in animated conversations along both sides of the car. But her thoughts were not on food. She ordered the first item on the list and handed the menu to the waiter.

Her eyes returned to Adam as he placed his order.

He had matured. His single-breasted coat and tie contributed to his look of success. His once-mischievous grin had grown into a manly smile. He had a more determined look.

She folded her hands in her lap and looked him straight in the eyes. "You never even said goodbye."

Adam glanced down at his plate. "I know. I regret that."

He leaned back in his chair, his eyes rising to meet hers. "After my father's murder, I didn't know what to do. As you know, my father was well known. Then one of the city magistrates seized our house to help repay the families my father had hurt. I just couldn't stay in Philadelphia. I needed to start over without someone staring at me and always thinking of me as they had thought of my father. I should have spoken to you, but I was too ashamed."

Adam sighed. "So, one morning I just packed up and went to New York. My skills as a typesetter allowed me to quickly land a job with the New York Tribune. But when I tried my hand at reporting, I discovered my real talent, journalism. So, for the last couple of years, I've been an investigative reporter. Broke a couple of big stories too, about crooked New York City politicians taking kickbacks from dirty businessmen.

"But then, four months ago, I was offered a feature writer's position with *The Nation*, a magazine out of Chicago."

Christine saw the gleam in Adam's eyes, how he had put his terrible past behind him. "What a wonderful opportunity! I'm sure you'll do well. I just hope being an investigative reporter doesn't put you in harm's way."

"I've got to watch my step, I'll admit," Adam answered. "Like my new series on corruption. When you deal with the criminal underworld, you have to look past what's on the surface to what's underneath, pardon the pun."

Then his expression relaxed as a smile formed. "But what about you? Why a train to Chicago?"

Christine told him about her father's death and how she was now on her own. She told him about Paradise and how she was determined to move on and accept her Aunt Agnes' offer.

Adam nodded. "You never were one to back down. I've thought about you often. Wondered how you were, what you were doing. You know, Christine, we were the best of friends."

They stared at each other in a moment of awkward silence as

the waiter arrived and placed their plates on the table.

After thanking the waiter, Adam smiled and raised his water glass. "Here's to the past and lessons learned."

Christine returned a smile. "And to the future and new beginnings."

With a soft clink, she touched her glass to his.

CHAPTER 5

WELCOME TO CHICAGO

ADAM woke at the jostling of the train as it rounded a steep bend in the tracks. Close to twenty-four hours had passed since the train chugged out of Paradise. He'd had a hard time sleeping in the unyielding coach seats. They seemed to get harder with each passing mile.

Christine rested her head on a small pillow pressed up against the window. Sunlight spilled through the trees and dappled her face in alternating flickers of brightness and shadow.

As Adam stretched and rubbed his face, Christine slowly opened her eyes, then scooted into a proper sitting position.

"I'm glad the senator agreed to switch cars," Christine said as she raised a hand to her mouth and fought back a yawn.

"So am I," Adam said, reaching into the pocket of his coat for the two apples and the bag of peanuts he'd saved from dinner.

"Care for one?" he asked, holding up a shining Macintosh.

"Thanks," she replied. "After such a big dinner last night, an apple sounds perfect."

Adam returned the remaining apple to his pocket, then rustled open the bag of peanuts.

Just before noon, the brakes squealed and the train decreased its speed. Adam watched Christine turn toward the window. He leaned forward and looked over her shoulder as they approached a station. He knew they were still an hour or so from Chicago.

A white brick wall twice the height of a man stretched at least a hundred yards to the right and left of the train station, parallel to the tracks. Every several hundred feet, the wall connected to even taller brick towers. Five cobblestoned entrance roads twisted through perfectly manicured grass to five sets of iron gates. A brick archway spanned each set of gates.

The train screeched into the station. Hanging from the platform ceiling every fifty feet or so, rectangular signs with the words NEW EDEN welcomed arrivals. Atop the entrance to the station building another sign displayed the same name in larger letters.

Workers dressed in dark slacks and brown shirts pushed carts and drove wagons. Others swept the platform and emptied trash containers. One man painted the wood trim on the station's windows.

Across from the train station platform, above the center of the third and middle archway, were wrought iron letters, announcing yet again the words NEW EDEN to visitors.

Adam craned his neck and looked to the far right. Another set of train tracks split off from the main line and curved into a separate entrance. Beyond the split in the tracks and the high wall, he could make out the rooflines of large warehouses and lazy columns of smoke drifting skyward from tall smokestacks.

Christine tapped Adam on the arm. "Look!" She drew his attention to the main gates as the train slowed to a stop.

A tall, angular man wearing white pants with a deep purple shirt and a white clerical collar stood with his arms crossed over his chest. A small gust of wind stirred the thick mane of white hair that hung over his shoulders, but did not disturb his resolute gaze. Beside him, a man with brown skin, black pants, and a gray shirt made notes in a small ledger. The man in the gray shirt paused to scratch his neatly sculpted and closely trimmed beard.

Beyond the two men, Christine's and Adam's eyes followed a

long walkway that led through an immaculate lawn. Two men dressed in dark slacks and light brown shirts tended a circular flower garden with a large, pink-veined marble fountain. Beyond the fountain, they could see the front of a long, three-story brick building with two-story wings and a slate roof. White, semicircular steps led to tall open doors. A woman in a blue blouse led two orderly rows of children up the steps and into the building.

"What is New Eden?" Christine asked.

Adam reached into his coat pocket and pulled out a schedule. He pointed to a line on the sheet. "A town. It's listed right here, New Eden. A 15-minute stopover."

"I've never seen a town like this," Christine said softly, her face close to the window. She smiled. "It's so beautiful. The lawns and gardens, the look of fresh paint everywhere, the clean walkways. It reminds me of the Centennial Exposition."

"It's nice," Adam replied leaning back, studying her smiling face in the window's reflection.

When they passed the end of the wall surrounding New Eden, his thoughts shifted to Chicago, now only 20 miles away.

A city known for its wind and its railroads, its grain and its stockyards, its gambling, its crime and the Great Fire of 1871.

And now, Christine.

Their train pulled into Chicago right on time at 1 p.m.

Adam helped Christine with her bags. She asked him to hold the paperbound journal about the history of Paradise while she adjusted her hat. Christine explained how she had become Aunt Mildred's courier and had to return the journal to Aunt Agnes.

For a second, Christine's mention of Paradise clicked with something else in Adam's thoughts. But before his trained journalist instincts could connect the still-forming impressions, Christine exited the station and walked into a bustle of passengers jostling for cabs.

Adam led Christine toward the left end of the raised wooden platform until they found an empty cab.

He noted the confident way Christine instructed the driver. Adam chuckled at her determination. She had matured into a young woman since the last time they had been together.

He closed the cab door for her.

Christine brought her cheerful face up to the open window. "I'm going to stop and pick up a dried-flower arrangement for my aunt. I hope she likes it."

Adam grinned. "I'll call on you in a couple of days, after we've both settled in."

The driver snapped the reins. Adam stepped back and fingered the slip of paper on which Christine had written her aunt's address. The cab pulled away.

Christine leaned up again to the window and waved.

Waving back, Adam pondered his chance meeting with Christine on the train. Providence, he thought. God has surely brought us together after four years of being apart.

He watched her cab rumble toward Chicago's North Side. Though most of the North Side had burned to the ground in the Great Fire, the several blocks where her aunt lived had gone unscathed.

Adam glanced at the address on the slip of paper—Miss Agnes Thompson, 1644 Lincoln Avenue—then stuffed it into his coat pocket. He stepped to the curb and signaled a waiting cab. Arrangements had been made for him to stay at the Phillips' Boardinghouse on the South Side, opposite the direction in which Christine was now headed. But at least he could walk to the building where The Nation's offices were located.

He climbed into the cab and spoke to the driver through a small rectangular window in the front divider. "Phillip's Boardinghouse, please."

The driver tipped his hat and shook the reins. The cab rocked through a sharp dip in the street, then jerked forward and headed north.

Confused, Adam spoke to the driver.

"Why are we heading north? I'm supposed to be staying in the South Side."

The driver glanced back over his shoulder. The ends of his red handlebar moustache drooped as he frowned. "You said Phillip's Boardinghouse, correct? On Madison Street?"

Adam pulled a small, black notebook from his coat pocket and flipped directly to a marked page. "Yes, on Madison."

"Well, sonny, you tell me." The driver scratched the stubble on his chin. "I'm just the cabby."

Weighing the options, Adam quickly made his decision.

"Keep going. At least I've got a room waiting for me. Plus I forwarded my trunk there several weeks ago. I'll just have to make new arrangements tomorrow and move in closer."

The cabby twisted around and laughed. "Best not eat her cooking then, or you'll be hooked like a fish on a line! Boarders 'round here would kill for a room and a regular meal of the best home-style cookin' in all of Chicago!"

Adam entered his fourth-floor room and set his suitcase on the end of the poster bed. His room was tastefully furnished with a wardrobe in one corner, a desk and lamp in the other, a washstand and his private water closet—a luxury he had not expected. On the wall above the desk was a small bookshelf, and on the wall to the right, a window facing east.

Interested in the view, Adam stepped to the window, pulled back the curtain, and stuffed his hands into his pants pockets.

Off to the south he could see Chicago's rising new cityscape and tall, stately buildings. Adam knew most of the downtown had already been rebuilt. Unlike New York or Philadelphia, Chicago had been reborn from the ashes of the most famous firestorm in the nation's history.

"So you're the Queen of the West?" Adam asked out loud as his eyes followed the street eight blocks straight east to white-capped Lake Michigan. The lake was much larger than he had imagined. Choppy green-gray waters close to the shore stretched and smoothed all the way to the horizon. The sight of both small skiffs and broad steamers brought back pleasant memories of New York Harbor and the Atlantic Ocean.

Movement on the street below caught Adam's attention.

A cab pulled up to the curb in front of a large, two-story brick estate that filled a corner lot, one block to the southeast. The driver climbed down to the sidewalk, then opened the door to the cab. A young lady with a valise and handsome bunch of dried flowers stepped out onto the sidewalk.

Adam's mouth dropped. Christine?

He pulled his hands from his pockets, unlocked and yanked open the window. He leaned on the windowsill for a better look.

Adam chuckled. If he had any doubts about God's providence before, he doubted no longer. Phillip's Boardinghouse was one block from where Christine would be living.

He lifted his eyes to the sky and thanked his Creator.

The cabby lowered Christine's suitcases to the sidewalk, then carried them to the front steps.

She handed him his fare plus a tip. "Thanks."

Christine turned around. The sandstone-colored brick house, with four tall oak trees at each corner, took up most of the lot. She counted twelve stately, curtained windows in the center section of the house, six to a floor, separated by a massive front door of dark, fancily carved wood and a small decorative balcony on the second floor. Each of the house's square-shaped wings, right and left, had four windows. Twenty windows in all—on just the front of the house! How could Aunt Agnes possibly afford such a place?

Amazed, Christine walked up the steps and reached for the doorbell. But before she could ring it, the door swung open.

A husky woman with blond hair and plain features greeted her with a wry smile. She wore a long black dress and a white apron. "You must be Christine Thompson. Please come inside. You've been expected. Your suitcases will be handled for you."

"Thank you." Christine stepped across the threshold. The two-story foyer opened to a rose marble floor and a sweeping mahogany staircase, reminding Christine of several prominent Philadelphia homes she had visited with her father. Evidently, Aunt Agnes had more money than Christine had thought.

"Follow me please," the maid instructed politely, taking Christine's valise and flowers from her hands. Christine did not argue. She followed the maid into a large drawing room.

A highly polished grand piano sat in one corner. Four gold side chairs and a deep-red velvet sofa were positioned at a respectful distance from an oversized fireplace. On the sofa table stood two tall oriental vases with a large Chinese bowl in between. Light entered from three of the twenty floor-to-ceiling windows Christine had seen from the outside.

The maid continued through the room and turned to their right. She opened French doors and led Christine down a hall.

"Miss Thompson is in her study."

The maid stopped at a doorway and held out her right arm, motioning for Christine to enter. Taking a deep breath, Christine stepped forward into the room. To her left, a marble fireplace housed a glowing gas fire. To her right, bookshelves spanned the entire length of the wall. In the middle of the room sat a large mahogany desk and behind it a slight, silver-haired lady carefully making notations in a ledger. The drapes on the windows behind her were fully open.

Aunt Agnes looked up, removing her glasses and allowing them to hang from her neck on a braided gold chain. She wore a simple gray dress with a plaid charcoal-colored shawl wrapped around her narrow shoulders. She tipped her head slightly to the right.

"Christine, my dear, how was your trip?"

Christine did not expect her aunt to look so young. Wrinkles crowded her eyes, but her blue eyes sparkled. She had a straight, thin nose and a narrow mouth—at the moment, anyway, with her lips pressed together so thoughtfully.

"Everything went fine, Aunt Agnes. Though I'll say Chicago is a world apart from Philadelphia. And even more so, Paradise."

To Christine's surprise, Aunt Agnes laughed. How could so loud a sound come from so small a woman!

Aunt Agnes rose from behind her desk and approached Christine. "Indeed. Chicago is the city of the future; Philadelphia is a city of the past. And Paradise, Paradise is—"

Aunt Agnes stopped, then gave Christine a firm hug before stepping back. "I'm so pleased you are here."

"You have a lovely home, Aunt Agnes."

Her aunt bobbed her head slightly. "I have carefully managed my assets. Calculated investments, thriftiness when need be, and an eye toward the future have always been my philosophy.

"As you must be aware, your father and I never agreed on how he chose to spend his inheritance. He invested in people who could never give him a return. Just like your Uncle John, who wasted his money on fool's gold. Then he went off to war, got himself blown to smithereens at Gettysburg, and left your proud Aunt Mildred too poor to leave Paradise."

Aunt Agnes stepped back around her desk. "At least, your father had the good sense to plan for this eventuality. The money he sent me for you will be yours when you find a place of your own."

Christine's eyes widened. "My father sent you money?"

"You didn't know?" Aunt Agnes seemed surprised herself.

Christine shook her head.

"Matthew wired me funds every month for the last four years." Aunt Agnes sighed. "He gave me clear instructions to set up an account for you. He knew that he was dying."

This new knowledge struck hard. Christine lowered her eyes and folded her hands in front of her.

"Be assured. I will help you invest your trust fund." Aunt Agnes sat down and put on her eyeglasses. "Dinner is at six."

The maid appeared without being called. Aunt Agnes spoke without looking up.

"Please show Christine to her room and make sure she is entirely comfortable after her long trip."

CHAPTER 6

THE PATH OF PROGRESS

As heavy, flowered drapes covering the dining room windows were were pulled back, a fiery sunset beneath a thick bank of clouds was revealed. A large crystal chandelier hung above the long dining room table where Christine and Aunt Agnes sat at opposite ends. Her aunt's high-necked, royal blue gown surely cost more than all of Christine's clothes combined.

"Aunt Mildred asked me to give you this package." Christine held up the paperbound journal.

"Ingrid," Aunt Agnes called softly toward the kitchen.

Christine handed the package to the maid who appeared quickly at her side. Ingrid hurried through a swinging door into the kitchen. Christine could hear the crinkle of paper. Less than fifteen seconds later, Ingrid swung the door open and presented the journal to Aunt Agnes.

Aunt Agnes did not take the book from Ingrid, but reached for the reading glasses that hung from a gold chain around her neck. She glanced at the cover. A tight smile creased her face.

"What did Mildred tell you about this book?" she asked, peering at Christine over the flat, top rim of her eyeglasses.

"Nothing at all," Christine replied as Ingrid patiently held the book. "She asked me to return it, but only in passing, the night before I left. I didn't actually see the journal until the next morning, when Melody took me to the train station. She said her mother didn't care for it very much."

Aunt Agnes shook her head. "Hmm. I suspected as much. Your aunt is much too proud to face the truth about Paradise."

Aunt Agnes straightened her shoulders and sat erect in her chair, looking down her thin nose and grabbing the armrests in a queenly fashion. She glanced up at Ingrid. "Return the book to the library."

Christine's eyebrows rose. She masked her frown by raising her glass and taking a sip of water. Proud? Just look in the mirror, Aunt Agnes! she thought to herself.

"Feel free to read the journal, Christine," Agnes continued. "A dear friend discovered it at an estate sale some months ago. As a regular attendee of my weekly parlor meetings, she knew of your aunt and uncle's foolish involvement with Paradise."

Aunt Agnes' face soured momentarily, as if her association with Aunt Mildred was like biting into a lemon. She cleared her throat, then resumed. "But, I will say no more. From your expression behind that glass, I can see that you disapprove of my comments."

"Oh, Aunt Agnes—" Christine blushed, lowering her glass and finding herself at an uncomfortable loss for words.

Her aunt relaxed her grip on the armrests and smiled, the tone in her voice softening. "No need to apologize. Unfairly, I put you on the spot with your dear aunt. Living alone, I am quite accustomed to say whatever is on my mind. Bear with me. You have come of age and must form your own opinions about Paradise, about womanhood and, quite frankly, about all other matters."

Christine felt the heat fade from her cheeks. Stunned but somewhat relieved by Aunt Agnes' straightforward speaking, she nodded in agreement. Compared to Aunt Mildred, Aunt Agnes understood and talked openly about the issues that mattered most to Christine.

Aunt Agnes folded her hands loosely in her lap. A faint smile stole across her face.

"You will soon learn, that here, in my house, you will not receive a drop of sympathy for past trials. No, here you will receive only rivers of encouragement to better yourself, with a mind to the future."

Her aunt lightly touched her forefinger to her temple. "Your ability to control your health, your life and your destiny is directly linked to your ability to think correctly."

Again, Aunt Agnes touched her temple.

Christine sat patiently, her hand still wrapped around her glass, grasping for meaning in her aunt's words.

Aunt Agnes sighed. "Twelve years ago we ended a terrible war. But men are never truly freed by bayonet, sword or cannon fire. Neither are they freed by advancements in machinery, physical sciences or horticulture."

Christine immediately thought about the Centennial Exposition back in Philadelphia. She wanted to ask her aunt what she meant, but before she could ask, Aunt Agnes continued, her voice rising.

"No! Men can be freed only through a Divine Science, through the restructuring of our mental processes. We need the divine mind, God's mind. And this, Christine, is what the future of man is all about."

Aunt Agnes gazed across the room at the fireplace. "Through millions of years man evolved from ape to human. Darwin calls it evolution. Others simply call it progress. Regardless of one's choice of words, the truth is clear: the Christian religion is evolving, Christine. From an old-time religion to a Divine Science of the future. Physical healing is not something you need doctors or medicines to cure. There is a science of health. A science of life. A science that comes from God. Sin and sickness, disease and death are the enemies of Truth. Heaven is not just some place we go after we die. We can enjoy heaven right here on earth, right now."

Goosebumps ran up Christine's arms as she listened in rapt silence at her aunt's words, words that were very strange but very familiar at the same time. Darwin was a crank, her father had said, whose false ideas about man and God would soon be rejected. Why then was Aunt Agnes talking positively about both Darwin and God in the same breath?

"Hold to your ideas of the past if you so choose, Christine, but I hope you choose the better path, the path of human progress." Aunt Agnes rose from her chair.

"Breakfast is always served at seven-thirty sharp."

Her final words spoken, Aunt Agnes charged purposefully out of the room and down the hall toward her study.

Adam Vestry stared east from his window. The last rays of the setting sun cast a dark rose hue on the front of Aunt Agnes' house one block away. Lights burned on both floors of the north wing. The smoke curling upward from the center chimney caught and reflected the sun's final glimmerings, drifting eastward toward the lake before disappearing into the air.

The city of Chicago lay regally against the shores of Lake Michigan, where lights from thousands of homes and buildings gleamed like some impossibly large necklace of multicolored gems, stretching east to the lake and south into the distance. Scattered pockets of darkness amid the glistening lights revealed hollowed-out stone foundations, crumbled brick walls, and piles of hardened cinders still remaining from the Great Fire.

Adam glanced down at the briefing papers his boss at *The Nation* had rushed him by courier earlier in the afternoon and which he had just finished reading.

Beginning on Sunday night, October 8, 1871, and lasting just 24 hours, the Great Fire had incinerated 18,000 buildings, killed 300 people and left another 100,000 homeless. But in just five years, nearly all those dark pockets had been systematically filled with newly constructed churches, schools, manufacturing plants, warehouses, offices, libraries, municipal buildings, one-room shanties, small houses, apartments and winged, multistory mansions just like Christine's aunt's. Chicago labored hard, rebuilding itself day by day, sweaty brow by sweaty brow, hard-earned dollar by hard-earned dollar, structure by structure.

For some, the Great Fire did not destroy their careers or fortunes. Some had seen their careers in business and in the city government become even more influential and their fortunes grow even larger. And when vast amounts of money regularly passed from hand to hand, corruption soon followed.

Worse came to worst when finally, in 1873, after a decade of increased crime and vice across the city, Mike McDonald's Democrats got their candidate, Harvey Colvin, elected as mayor of Chicago. For the first time, organized crime had official control of Chicago's politics.

But this year, the people of Chicago had come to their senses and elected reformist Mayor Monroe Heath. And Mayor Heath, backed by Adam's magazine, *The Nation,* and other anticrime organizations and leaders, had vowed to fight the corruption the previous mayor had allowed to permeate the city.

Adam crossed his arms and considered his new assignment. Working with Mayor Heath, *The Nation* would help expose the gamblers and politicians who had lied, cheated, and misused their power to defraud the city and people of Chicago. Adam knew this dangerous assignment would be his greatest challenge as an investigative journalist.

Wary, but not afraid, Adam stared at the front of Christine's aunt's house until the rosy glow of dusk faded into gray. He turned and closed the window, then pulled his watch from his vest pocket and popped it open.

His new "source" would be arriving any moment. The note from his boss had only mentioned the name Joey. Newspapers and magazines relied on sources like Joey to help them get real-time information about what was happening on the streets. The mayor's office and the police probably thought of Joey as an informant or a snitch, but neither Adam nor his magazine liked that term. The term "source" sounded much more professional.

Joey what? Adam wondered to himself. One rarely ever learned a source's full name, much less a real name. And when the contact's identity was discovered, it was usually at the city morgue—from a relative who had come to claim the body. Being a source was far more dangerous than being an investigative reporter!

Adam snapped the watch shut and slipped it into his pocket. He grabbed his small black notebook from the end table by his bed and stuffed it into the breast pocket of his dark wool coat.

Feeling his pockets, Adam made sure that he had his wallet, his pocketknife, his new press pass, and, most importantly, a thick wad of cash. Adam grinned, turned down the two oil lamps, then headed across the creaky floor for the door to his room.

As he reached for the doorknob, three knocks startled him.

"Hey, it's me. Joey," a voice called quietly from the hall.

Adam opened the door. For a second, the hall appeared empty. Then, to the right in the stairwell doorway, he noticed a short, wiry man with close-cropped curly black hair.

"Nice room, Mr. Vestry, let me tell you. Right by the stairs." Joey smiled, showing a full set of amazingly straight teeth beneath a narrow, crooked nose. His eyes, dark like his hair, peered out from under a high forehead and retreating hairline. Joey had to be ten years older than Adam, maybe more.

Adam placed Joey's accent immediately. New York, had to be.

Joey nodded as if he knew exactly what Adam had been thinking. "Yeah, I know. But don't believe it. I don't come from New York. I just want everybody to think that I do."

He tipped his head in the direction of the stairs.

"Better hurry. Gotta get there early if you wanna a ringside seat."

Adam locked the door to his room. "So, you're taking me to a circus?"

"A circus!" Joey laughed, his eyes brightening suddenly. "I see you're a man with a sense of humor. Yeah, we're going to a circus, all right. Just be careful and don't go sticking your head into the lion's mouth on your first night here in Chicago!"

CHAPTER 7
FACES

IN the narrow, poorly lit tavern known as Slippery Ed's, the dozen or so tables and booths were two-thirds filled. The smell of smoke and sweat tainted the air. A pot-bellied stove near the right wall heated the room. Six dusty-faced men in grimy overalls crowded up to a chest-high bar at the far end of the tavern. They joked and laughed after a hard day's work at the furniture factory next door. But Slippery Ed's customers were a sundry lot. Three men in dark suits and vests not unlike Adam's played cards at a table to their left. In the near corner sat a man with a black top hat and cape slung casually over the empty chair beside him. His hands wrapped around a tall, half-empty mug. Men from every level of society congregated at Slippery Ed's: bluebloods, trades men, clerks and workmen alike.

Adam shot Joey an incredulous look. He leaned forward over the small, cloth-covered table. Even though he whispered, he could not conceal his interest in Joey's latest revelation. "You actually lived in the Underworld? Right here in what used to be called Conley's Patch?"

Joey shrugged his shoulders as if to say, yeah, no big deal.

Adam followed Joey's glance out the front window and down lamp-lit Fifth Street, former home to Conley's Patch, Chicago's once-notorious vice district. From his briefing paper, Adam knew that before the Great Fire, Conley's Patch was home to a vast, rambling building made of wood, brick and stone called Roger's Barracks. Named after its infamous builder, Roger Plant, the old manufacturing building had so many additions that by the time of the Great Fire, it filled over half a city block. But Roger's Barracks, just like nearly eighteen thousand other buildings, had burned to ashes in just minutes.

"Good ol' Roger took anybody in," Joey went on to say, "anybody in trouble with the law, that is, as long as they had plenty of money or information he could use, he had plenty of space. Space for every kind of business in his Barracks, over a hundred rooms. And he had sixty more down in the Underworld, a maze of tunnels that ran through the building's foundations.

"I tell you, a man could get lost and never be seen again if he stumbled into the wrong room at the wrong time. Gambling, drinking, making bribes and cutting deals—for the criminal element, Roger had it all."

Joey sipped his coffee, then lowered the mug to the table. For several seconds, he just stared into the steaming drink. Adam sensed pain lurking behind Joey's eyes but decided not to ask.

"So anyways," Joey continued, looking up at last. For a second Adam thought he saw tears in Joey's eyes, but his source then blinked the evidence away.

"The Fire only slowed down crooked men like 'ol Roger. He was just one of a dozen powerful men who made their fortunes from card tables and roulette wheels. Now, it's men like Mike McDonald who control the gambling and the deal making in this city."

"There's a sucker born every minute," Adam said softly.

Joey grinned. "You know it was Ol' Mike who coined that phrase, not P.T. Barnum, the famous circus promoter."

Adam looked up. "Didn't know that. But unfortunately, it's true. People will believe anything these days. Just call it 'progress' or 'evolution' and people perk right up. No one seems interested in the values and beliefs that helped make our nation so strong. It's hard to believe how far we've fallen in just one hundred years."

A loud creak caused Adam and Joey to look up. The tavern door swung open. Out the window, Adam saw four men standing at the door. They entered single file. The first, a scrawny, balding man with round spectacles, wore a knee-length tan coat.

The second, a tall, broad-shouldered man with a pockmarked face and a dark scowl stopped just inside the doorway, slipped off his black overcoat and then allowed the third man to pass by. From the bulge near the left armpit in the pockmark-faced man's black suit, Adam knew he carried a large-caliber handgun and wanted everyone to know it.

Adam drew a sharp breath—not because of the gun, but from seeing the face of the third man as he walked by. Adam focused on his closely cropped and sculpted beard, his brown skin and now, after seeing him close up, his familiar face.

He had not recognized the freedman when he had seen him earlier in the day, when the man had been dressed in black pants and a gray shirt, standing in front of a train station and making notes on a clipboard. Christine would have seen him too as she looked out the window from the train, but she would have no reason to remember the man's face.

A fourth man, wearing a dark pinstriped suit, filed in last and followed the other two to a booth twenty feet away. Adam kept his face aimed down as if he were deep in thought. The man with the sculpted beard had sat down and was facing directly toward Adam.

"Well," Joey whispered, his voice low enough that the pockmark-faced man standing by the door wouldn't hear, "Those are the men I brought you here to see. Forget the big goon to my right—no brain, just muscles. It's the other three that matter. Mister Spectacles is a bookkeeper for Mike McDonald. Mister Pinstripes works in the mayor's office. And the guy with the beard represents a major business enterprise involved with Chicago's rebuilding effort. They've been meeting regularly for several weeks. It's the black guy you need to follow up on. I can tell you his name and where he comes from. His—"

Adam cut in before Joey could finish. "Lucius Morris, and he represents the interests of a town called New Eden."

Joey coughed, his eyes widening suddenly. "Hey, I wanted to make some money off that name! How do you know him? And how do you know about New Eden?"

Adam continued to look down, worried that Lucius might see and recognize his face. "Don't worry. You'll get paid all the same. Let's just say I've met Mr. Morris before in less than pleasant circumstances. You might even say life-threatening circumstances. I'll have to explain later."

"So that's why you've got your face buried in that cup of coffee." Concern rippled across Joey's face. "Hey, I'm cooked if any of those three men connect you to me."

Adam nodded. "Maybe it's time we leave."

"You got that right," Joey replied, already on his feet and putting on his cap. He tugged the brim until it shadowed his eyes, then headed for the door with his head slightly down.

Frowning, Adam followed without looking up. He pulled the wad of cash from his pocket and dropped two bills on the table to cover their meal. Adam didn't have time to wait for change.

Then he stepped past the pockmark-faced man and out the creaking door into the night.

"Good morning," Aunt Agnes said as Christine sat down at the breakfast table. A copy of the Friday morning newspaper lay folded beside her aunt's plate.

"What would you like to eat, dear?"

Surprised that she had a choice, Christine floundered for a

moment. "I guess a soft-boiled egg and a roll or fruit would be fine. And a cup of coffee, please."

Aunt Agnes nodded to Ingrid, who headed for the kitchen. On the table in front of Christine lay a second copy of the newspaper, folded back to reveal a list of job postings.

"When do you plan to begin looking for work?" Aunt Agnes asked, gazing seriously at her charge over the top of her reading glasses.

Christine had never considered the possibility that she would have to look for employment the very day after she arrived!

Flustered again, she fumbled over her words. "I . . . I don't know. I thought maybe I would take a couple days and learn about the city, you know, see what kind of opportunities might be available first, before I jump into anything."

"Hmm. I don't want you frittering away opportunities, which is why I hope you don't mind that I've taken the liberty to have Ingrid mark several promising offers. Besides, finding a proper position may take longer than you think. And what better way to learn the city."

Christine sat back as Ingrid brought her a soft-boiled egg, two hard rolls and a small bowl with peeled pear halves. Glancing at the paper beside her, Christine saw three circled postings.

"Thank you, Ingrid," Christine said, gladly turning her attention from jobs to food. She broke open the egg. The white was perfectly soft.

"Also," her aunt added, closing her paper, "tomorrow afternoon we will attend a tea at the Forsythes'. The tea will give you a chance to meet the most progressive women in Chicago."

After finishing her breakfast, Christine picked up the paper and looked at the first circled ad. A Methodist minister on the West Side of Chicago wanted a nanny to help with his seven children, starting with one-month-old twins on up to age seven.

Yikes! Christine winced through her smile. Seven children!

Thoughts of endless burpings, milk bottles and sloppy diaper pails, coupled with the clinging arms and hands of attention-seeking toddlers, made her eyes move quickly down the page.

The second advertisement, posted by Chicago Mercy Hospital on the East Side, sought a nurse's assistant trainee. Christine paused. Though she'd never considered herself squeamish, she wasn't sure she would want to be around the sick and dying every day—much less the surgeries. She'd heard too many Civil War stories about performing amputations, stitching wounds and setting shattered bones in Northern and Southern field hospitals.

On the other hand, she wasn't sure if she wanted to attend many of Aunt Agnes' afternoon teas, either!

With sudden renewed interest, she turned her attention back to the third circled ad.

WANTED! INDIVIDUALS AND FAMILIES TO HELP REBUILD CHICAGO. OPPORTUNITIES OF A LIFETIME. JOIN NEW EDEN, AMERICA'S FASTEST-GROWING, PROGRESSIVE COMMUNITY. NEEDED THIS WEEK: TEACHER FOR CHILDREN GRADES 1-6. APPLY IN PERSON. ROOM AND BOARD INCLUDED.

Christine leaned back in her chair and sipped her coffee. New Eden—why she and Adam had passed through New Eden just the day before!

She remembered its massive iron gates, trimmed lawns and swept walkways. From the train station to the gardens, everything looked clean and well-maintained. And the trip to Chicago took less than an hour.

She held the paper up and reread the ad. Opportunities of a lifetime. America's fastest-growing, progressive community.

"Teacher," Christine whispered.

"What did you say?" Aunt Agnes asked as she folded her napkin and placed it on the table.

"Oh, excuse me," she replied through a grin. "I was just talking to myself."

A teacher, with room and board included. She could save nearly everything she earned. Aunt Agnes would surely approve, not only of her position as a teacher, but also of the monetary benefits of free housing and free meals on top of an honest wage.

And besides, whether she got the position or not, responding to the ad would give her a chance to visit New Eden and find out more about the fascinating walled town.

A beautiful town. A pleasing job. A chance to make her own way. Could this be the opportunity she had been hoping for?

CHAPTER 8
NEW EDEN

IN downtown Chicago the offices and production room of *The Nation* occupied the entire three floors of the Milborne Building.

Adam Vestry's corner office overlooked Market Street and faced the Illinois Trust and Savings Bank on the opposite corner of the four-way intersection. The new bank, chartered in June 1873, had survived the October panic of that year and now flourished. Oscar Milborne, a trustee of the Illinois Trust and Savings Bank and owner of *The Nation*'s office building, was the silent partner of David Welch, *The Nation*'s managing editor and Adam's boss. To say the least, Adam did not fear *The Nation*'s financial stability.

On Friday morning at seven sharp, Adam stepped into his office. He removed his hat, slipped out of his overcoat and hung it on the coat tree in the corner.

He walked to the window. Even from his third-floor vantage point, he could not see much more than the intersection and the several multistory buildings surrounding it. The sun had barely broken the horizon, but already the streets below were alive with activity. Wagons rumbled noisily by loaded down with wood, bricks and stone. Horses and horse-drawn trolleys, carriages and buggies bore straight-backed passengers to their workplaces. Fighting the gusting winds, pedestrians from all walks of life scurried through the intersection in every direction, clutching black top hats, brown bowlers, plaid caps, bright silk scarves and plain woolen shawls.

Adam pulled out his chair and sat down. Now sitting with his back to the outside world, he turned his attention to his office's large inner window that gave him a view of the fifteen desks and dozens of file cabinets in the pressroom. The pressroom was where the staff reporters, writers and artists worked day and night to create the thirty-two pages of magazine copy needed each week.

It was said that *The Nation* never slept.

His office had an oak desk, two file cabinets, a drafting table and stool, two oak side chairs, two lamps, and the coat tree in the corner. Other than the Swiss clock on his left and the oversized production calendar on his right, the green walls were bare, waiting for the watercolors or posters of Adam's choice.

Enthusiasm surged through Adam. He quietly thanked God for bringing him to Chicago. His new position would provide him with many opportunities, including travel. St. Louis, New Orleans and San Francisco were already on his schedule for early next year, assuming, that is, he completed his series of feature articles exposing the links between corrupt politicians, organized crime and big business.

The job paid well, too. If he didn't squander his income, he could save enough to think about building his own house by his next birthday! What positive change God had brought to his life: Philadelphia, then New York, and now Chicago. The trail of his past had almost disappeared.

Almost. Until last night in Slippery Ed's, when Lucius Morris walked past Adam and Joey's table.

Adam picked up a pencil and twirled it through his fingers.

Unlike four years ago in Philadelphia, Lucius now sported a beard and wore expensive clothes. Unlike four years ago, Lucius wasn't running in fear from the same evil men he foolishly worked for, wondering if he would get away or be shot in the back. Unlike four years ago, Lucius now held a position of some influence, at least in the underworld of crime that was somehow linked to the town called New Eden.

But Adam didn't want to think too much about the old days. His father's murder now seemed part of another lifetime, a time when Adam's entire world was turned upside down. Telling it all to Joey had been painful enough; he would not let those dark memories dominate him yet again.

Adam shook his head to clear the thoughts, then set his mind's eye on another face.

He pictured honest, blue eyes opening wide, a light sprinkle of freckles dancing across the gentle slope of a perfect nose, and long waves of strawberry-blond hair rustling in a soft breeze.

Now, after four years of being separated from Christine, Adam did not want to lose contact with her again. Maybe tomorrow, or the day after, he would stop by her aunt's house and arrange for a formal visit. Hopefully, the visit would be the first of many.

Adam smiled and glanced down at the short stack of papers in front of him, and the street address Joey had given him last night before they parted. Today's meeting with Joey promised to be very, very interesting.

A meeting in the Underworld.

Adam chuckled. The next time he met with Christine, what a story he'd have to tell!

Christine stepped down from the train onto the platform.

All her excitement and expectations about New Eden were just as she remembered from their arrival in Chicago two days ago. Unlike Paradise, New Eden's welcoming signs were brightly painted and lettered in flawless symmetry.

The grade of the road ran perfectly to the edge of the platform. Workers scurried about in dark trousers and nicely colored shirts.

Christine looked across the road at the expansive iron fence and tall brick towers. She could hardly see the other end. The immense proportions reminded her again of the awesome sights she had seen at the Centennial Exposition.

A wide avenue ran parallel to the fence. Railroad tracks broke off to Christine's right and curved toward a sixth entrance sealed off by large wooden doors.

Uncertain where she should go, Christine went back to the station. She approached the ticket window and spoke to an elderly mustached man wearing a pastel green shirt.

"I would like to respond to an advertisement in yesterday's paper for a teaching assignment."

"Yes ma'am," he said with a smile while pointing. "You need to go to Main Administration, that large brick building just inside those gates. Go inside to the admissions desk. Only desk. Can't miss it. Tell the person there what you just told me."

As Christine walked through the main gates and beneath the tall iron sign that read NEW EDEN, a man in a white suit stood and watched from a second-floor office window in the Main Administration Building.

Simon Friend, tall and angular, wore a purple shirt and a white clerical collar beneath his white jacket. He peered anxiously beneath white bushy eyebrows out the window toward the main gates. His smooth skin, the result of expensive oils and constant care, belied his actual age, which no one but he himself knew.

Ironically, his long white hair and eyebrows had nothing to do with his age. His blond hair had turned prematurely white in his twenties.

A knock on the office door caused Simon to turn around. Lucius Morris, his Chief of Security and second-in-command, entered the room, clipboard in hand. Lucius wore the standard issue light gray shirt and black pants worn by everyone in Security.

Simon crossed his arms and tapped his lower lip with a long, spindly finger. "Miss Wordsworth is on her way out of the building as we speak. Strike her name from the roster. And tell the People's Deputies that under no circumstances may she reenter the grounds of New Eden."

"It's already been done," Lucius replied. "And perhaps this will minimize our problem."

Lucius handed him Miss Wordsworth' clothbound diary.

Simon unlatched a small clasp and opened the diary. His eyebrows arched slightly as scanned the last few pages.

"Excellent, Mr. Morris. Another job well done. In fact, your recent hard work has earned you a fifteen percent increase in your allotment."

Simon smiled widely, walked to the desk and placed the diary in one of the drawers. "One more thing. Send one of your deputies to warn Miss Wordsworth, discreetly of course, that we have her diary and that we do not expect to hear even the faintest peep or complaint out of her. That will be all for now."

Christine followed the cobblestone pathway and took an extra moment to circle around a pink-veined marble fountain not far inside the main gates. As she did, a young woman about her age and carrying a valise brushed by her. Christine offered a cheerful greeting, but the teary-eyed woman kept her head lowered and continued walking briskly toward the main gates.

In moments, Christine reached Main Administration. The building had a simple but pleasing look, with various shades of light-red bricks. About the same size as Aunt Agnes' house, it had two additional floors and twice as many windows. Semicircular steps of white marble led up to the main doors.

Christine entered the building. As instructed, she found the admissions desk just inside.

"May I help you?" inquired a heavy-set man with oiled hair and a round, clean-shaven face. His starched gray shirt, buttoned at the neck, seemed just a little too tight.

"Yes, sir. My name is Miss Thompson. I'm here to inquire about the teaching position."

The man flipped through several sheets of paper attached to a wooden clipboard. "Yes, it's still open. But you'll need to see the Executive Manager. I'll direct you to his office, but first, please sign in."

The man pushed himself up from the chair and placed a bulky registration book in front of Christine. She dipped a pen into the inkwell and then recorded her name and address as required.

The man pointed across the large foyer. "The office is up those stairs to the left, second floor. First room on the right."

Christine climbed the winding staircase toward the second floor. At the landing, she met a serious-faced man with brown skin and a neatly trimmed beard, dressed similarly as the heavy-set man at the desk.

The man paused at the landing to let Christine pass comfortably by. Their eyes met briefly.

Turning to the right, Christine found the Executive Manager's office. A reed-thin elderly man wearing brown trousers and a light green shirt stood just outside an open door.

"Good morning, young lady. How may I help you?"

Christine again explained the reason she had come. The man directed her into the room and pointed to a leather armchair.

"Simon will be with you in a moment. Please be seated."

As Christine watched the elderly man return to his post outside the door, she suddenly realized that his outfit was identical to that of the man behind the ticket counter at the train station. Were they uniforms?

Christine sat in the armchair, facing a small mahogany desk

with two brass lamps. To her left was a closed door. To her right, a window overlooked the main gates and the train station.

On the wall behind the desk hung a painting, da Vinci's Last Supper. And beside the da Vinci, a portrait of President Rutherford B. Hayes. Beneath the paintings, a silver crucifix and a bronze ram stood on opposite ends of a long credenza. And between the cross and the ram, the largest Bible Christine had ever seen.

A drafting table took up the rest of the space on the left side of the room. On its angled surface, Christine could not help but see a detailed drawing titled Kiln #2. Next to the table six tightly rolled drawings leaned against the wall.

Suddenly, the door to her left opened wide, momentarily startling her.

Simon Friend smiled and stepped to his desk. He was six feet tall with long white hair that fell loosely over the shoulders of his white suit. His purple shirt and clerical collar only enhanced his stature. White bushy eyebrows arched over penetrating blue eyes and a lean, angular face.

"Miss Christine Thompson, what a pleasure to meet you. My name is Simon Friend. Follow me, please. And call me Simon. Mr. Friend will not do."

He led her through the door to his left. The adjacent room was slightly more spacious than his office, with a large sofa and two upholstered side chairs. Light entered from windows on two sides.

Simon motioned Christine to sit in one of the side chairs. "I consider interviews a most private matter."

Christine felt a bit uncomfortable being alone in a room with a strange man. But the door was open.

"So, Christine, you've come about our teacher's position," Simon said without asking a question. "But first, what do you think about New Eden?"

"Well, New Eden reminds me of the Centennial Exposition, of—of progress," she replied, not knowing what else to say.

Simon grinned. "I'll accept your statement as a compliment. I like to believe that New Eden is an example of progress."

Then he cocked his head slightly, eyeing her face. He clasped his spindly fingers together. His voice became serious.

"Tell me about yourself, daughter."

Daughter? Christine stiffened at the overly familiar reference.

Simon read her confusion. He nodded his head as if he understood. "You're puzzled by my choice of words. Allow me to explain.

"Are we not all brothers and sisters in the eyes of our Maker? And I, as the shepherd of our community, often assume a fatherly role with my flock. So, it's with fatherly attention that I refer to you as daughter. Do you object?"

"No, sir," Christine answered relaxing a little. "Actually, several of the elders in my father's church would sometimes address me that way."

"Good. Now, tell me something about yourself."

Christine told him about her upbringing, her mother's death and about her father's involvement with the Underground Railroad. Simon's eyebrows rose and fell as she explained how she worked closely with her father in the church and even taught Sunday school. She concluded with his funeral and her recent two-week visit with her aunt in Paradise, Pennsylvania.

Simon grew as still as a statue, except for his narrowing gaze and tiny folds of concern that appeared suddenly between his eyebrows. He politely cleared his throat, then finally spoke.

"I'm sorry to hear of your father's passing. Do I understand that you are now on your own?"

"Yes, I live with my aunt, in Chicago."

"I see." Simon shifted in his chair, edging forward. "You seem to be wonderfully qualified. And everyone needs a family. New Eden is like one big family, working hard and enjoying life together. Opportunities for advancement abound. When the interview is over, please take a brief tour of our community."

"Thank you, Mr. Friend."

"Again, please call me Simon."

Christine nodded hesitantly. "All right. Thank you, Simon."

"Now, let me tell you a small part of our town's history. Seven years ago, Providence saw fit to provide the funds for me to purchase the 1,600 acres upon which New Eden now sits. We work both with the Chicago authorities and with local builders to provide quality construction materials. In just seven years, we have developed into a major, if not the premier, source of supply.

"Even after the Great Fire, Chicago has continued to grow, mostly on the West Side and mostly from immigrants. Nearly two-thirds of Chicago's population are now foreigners—over 200,000 of them. And newcomers, often poor, can only afford to build homes made with wood. As the price of lumber and wood products has skyrocketed in recent years, New Eden has found itself in the right place at the right time."

Simon opened and spread his hands.

"October 8, 1871, the night of the Fire, is the night that New Eden truly discovered its destiny. While fires raged and devastated Chicago, I woke with an idea that would transform our little town. I would create a new kind of community where people could work together toward a common goal. A place where one's work is enhanced by the work of his brothers and sisters. A place to work hard and to produce. For didn't God say, 'Be fruitful, and multiply, and replenish the earth, and subdue it: and have dominion over every living thing that moveth upon the earth'?

"In the weeks following the Fire, hundreds of families flocked here. Families who had lost their homes and belongings, families whose fathers and mothers had no jobs, no place to go. We offered them the very thing they had just lost—we offered them hope. And we offered them a chance not only to rebuild their lives, but indirectly, Chicago, as well.

"Daughter, we practice our religion here, every day. We are not idle listeners, we are doers of the word."

Simon's words and passion suddenly reminded Christine of her father, of the beliefs that mattered to him and how he lived his life.

"Today, New Eden has its own rail system to import raw materials and to export finished goods. We make bricks, mill lumber, craft furniture, doors, windows, brass doorknobs, and even forge tools—nearly everything needed to rebuild Chicago. And we trained many of those same immigrant families to be carpenters, gas-fitters, garment workers, bricklayers and stone masons, upholsterers, machinists, and even artists."

Simon paused to draw in a breath.

"And just as important, we have our own schools and teachers for the education of our children. New Eden is helping Chicago rise from the ashes of judgment. We will restore her in body, mind and spirit, and make her the Queen of the West once again."

Simon's piercing gaze softened suddenly. His voice lowered to almost a whisper. "What do you say, Christine? Can I count on you for the job? For our children?"

"Your offer sounds inspiring Mr. Friend—I mean Simon. But I don't know any details about the position I'm applying for."

"What would you like to know?"

Embarrassed but determined, she forced out her question. She dared not return to Chicago and face Aunt Agnes without knowing details about wages.

"I hate to ask, but how much does the position pay?"

"I'll be blunt, Miss Thompson. Those who work here, live here. As of this morning, a space has become available in the home of a couple who are longtime friends of mine. They live two blocks from the school. Their fine home has a dormer suite with two adjacent rooms that you can decorate however you wish.

"And through a monthly allotment, New Eden provides you

with clothes to wear and food to eat. Based on performance and tenure, we reward hard-working employees with cash bonuses that can be saved or spent, however the employee chooses.

"So, do you want the position?"

"I'll need a day or two to think about it," Christine answered slowly. "But I'm very thankful for the interview, regardless of my decision."

Simon nodded. "I understand. Life as I have described it is very different from how most people choose to live. But it doesn't take long to see the benefits of the equality you'll find here.

"And you won't find overcrowded or run-down neighbor hoods, smoky bars or gambling rooms, pickpockets, or a single piece of trash anywhere in New Eden. Personal responsibility is honored here. On your tour, stop and speak with anyone you see. I'll tell you what they'll say."

Simon paused for a moment, as if searching for the right words. Then his eyes gleamed.

"They will tell you that New Eden is all about progress."

Christine smiled cheerfully. "Thank you."

Simon winked. "I'll tell you what. Since I like you, I'll hold the teacher's position open for three days. No one else will be allowed to apply. Is my offer agreeable to you?"

"That is very kind. And thank you again."

"It's no problem." Simon stood up and bowed. Christine rose from her chair.

"At the admissions desk, mention my name and ask for your tour. I'll send someone ahead to arrange for you to see the dormer rooms where you will live. You'll be pleased by the lovely view."

CHAPTER 9
UNDERWORLD

SIMON FRIEND watched Christine walk down the stairs.

Then he headed down the hall, past the room where he had met with her. Smiling, he stopped at a door farther down. A small brass plate above a paneled door read COMMUNICATIONS ROOM. Next to the door, a larger sign read STAFF ONLY.

A bald man with wire-rimmed glasses sat on the second of four tall stools. He faced a wide but shallow table set flush against the wall. Lucius Morris stood with his back to the table, arms crossed over his chest and clipboard. At the far end of the table, a broad man with a pockmarked face sat silently on the fourth stool and watched, his expression devoid of emotion.

Above the table were four shelves, each with twenty numbered slots. In some slots, slips of white paper stuck out. Above the four shelves were four clocks, each an hour apart.

The bald man glanced up at Simon, then continued tapping out the message on the telegraph transmitter. The receivers at each of the four stations were silent.

"The other men are on break," Lucius explained, handing Simon six sheets of paper. "We received the quotes eight minutes ago."

Simon silently read every word on each of the sheets before he looked up and spoke.

"All but one of the suppliers have dropped their prices. Unfortunately, the one who will not lower his quote makes up sixty percent of our bid. However, that little lumber mill is located only twenty miles west of here. Lucius, round up a team for tonight. You and your men have a little convincing to do. I just don't think our stubborn lumberman gets the point."

Looking down to the end of the table, Simon forced a smile.

"By tomorrow afternoon, I'll have the margins we need to complete the deal. Tell Mr. McDonald and our man in city hall that the delay is only temporary."

The man with the scarred face shook his head slowly. He spoke in a gravelly voice. "Big Mike ain't gonna like it. But bein' as it is, I'm sure he'd wanna know you yourself is lookin' out for his interests. Do you get my point?"

Simon fired Lucius a sharp glance, then nodded. "Tell Mr. McDonald I'll be there to make sure everything goes as planned. This deal will be concluded tomorrow. I guarantee it."

The Underworld!

Adam and Joey, their faces bathed in yellow light, both grinned as their lanterns drove back the darkness of the underground chamber.

They ignored the stench that rose from the stream of sewage trickling between their boots. They listened as a dozen tiny feet scuttled over crumbling concrete, then saw flashes of dark fur scurrying for the shadows. They stared at the jumble of broken chairs, smashed roulette wheels and dicing tables, rotting tapestries and glistening shards of liquor bottles littering the muddy water-stained floor.

"Don't like rats, never will," Joey grimaced, stopping for a moment until the faint scratching ceased. "OK, let's get on with it."

Adam smiled.

"The Great Fire," Joey explained as he rubbed his nose, "took out half the city. Most of the West Side was spared, including the house where General Sheridan, the Union Army hero, lived. City leaders begged him to help. He agreed and the mayor gave him control of the entire city. Sheridan declared martial law and U.S. soldiers were brought in.

"With Ol' Roger's gambling house up above nothin' but a big smoldering heap of ashes, Roger abandoned the Underworld. Over time, both police and vandals tore up the place."

Adam nodded as they stepped forward into the room. Glass crunched in the muck beneath their boots. Water dripped from cracks in the ceiling and fell into shallow pools with soft but regular plops. As their lantern light reached into an adjoining room, they heard the sounds of tiny claws moving rapidly once again.

They worked their way through the warren of rooms, pausing now and then to let the Underworld's furry occupants escape the spheres of yellow lantern light and the splash of boots in muddy water.

"How do you remember your way through here?" Adam asked, holding the lantern high.

"You forget. I knew the Underworld in its heyday, when it smelled of cigar smoke and booze instead of this stuff, whatever it is." Joey stepped carefully over a puddle of green-brown slime.

"And I came down here after the Fire, too. By myself, I might add. Furry little critters and all."

Joey ducked his head and peered beneath a fallen beam that angled down from ceiling to floor.

"Well, here we are…"

Joey went first, bending down and sliding between the beam and wall. "Watch your head! There's a rusty nail poking out."

Adam followed. Being taller than Joey, he had to work his way through more slowly. He kept his eyes trained forward on a two-inch nail that passed less than an inch from his face. Something brown, either rust or dried blood, stained the nail's jagged tip.

Adam stood and found himself in a small dingy room with no other exits. A decomposing Oriental rug lay in the center of the floor, bunched unevenly. A tattered cot, collapsed on one end, sat against the left wall. Grungy stacks of blankets were piled haphazardly in the corner next to a broken stool.

But Adam's attention had been drawn to the right side of the room. First, to a musty-looking but otherwise undamaged roulette wheel on a wooden table.

Then he looked to Joey, who had squatted, set his lantern on the floor, and was staring silently at what lay before him.

Adam inched forward, his eyes disbelieving but now locked on three gray-white skeletons stretched out on the floor in front of the table.

Bones. Human bones!

Joey poked at the nearest skull with a leg from the broken stool. "Don't spend any sympathy here. Bad lot, all three of 'em. Two were brothers. Thought they could double-cross Mike McDonald. But Mike's boys caught 'em red-handed on a train heading for San Francisco. With Mike's cash. Lots of it."

"And what about the third skeleton?" Adam asked, squatting beside Joey.

"A fool from city hall. He knew about the double-cross but didn't tell Mike. Claimed the brothers threatened his life. But Mike's boys found a stash of bills in the fool's apartment—stuffed in a mattress."

Joey sighed. "Mike's boys did in all three of them right here."

Adam set his lantern on the floor, then rested his elbows on his knees. "How do you know all of this?"

"Stupidest thing I've ever done—no, the second-most stupid thing."

Joey frowned and tossed the stool leg into the corner. Adam noticed Joey's eyes became teary for a moment, like they'd done at Slippery Ed's the other night.

"I was following a lead that sounded promising. In my trade, information is money. I was tailing Mike's boys the day they picked up the two brothers. They came here. I don't know how I kept up without being discovered. But I just kept following their trail of lantern light.

"Had a real close call, though, when a big fat rat shot out from behind a pile of garbage and darted under my foot. I clamped my teeth together. Couldn't afford to let go or yell. For a second, I thought I'd crushed it. But then that critter jumped right up and scrambled over the top of my boot! I can still feel its filthy little feet . . . ."

Joey swallowed hard. With the yellow lantern light shining upward from beneath his chin, his scrunched-up face and bulging eyes looked almost grotesque.

"Anyways, even though I couldn't get close enough to see 'em, I could sure hear 'em. Mike's men beat 'em up bad before it suddenly got real quiet. I heard a clacking sound, fast at first, but then slower and slower until it stopped.

Joey looked up at the roulette wheel. "Then I knew what was going on. Mike's boys were spinning that wheel. And what I heard was a roulette ball bouncing around until it slowed and finally dropped into a slot. Only that day, the stakes weren't gambling chips, but which of the three was going to get it first."

The hair on Adam's neck tingled and stood on end.

Joey grabbed his lantern.

"I brought you here so you'd know what happens to people who cross Mike McDonald. We're not playing just any old game."

He waved his lantern at the skeletons. "Like those three lying right there, we're gambling with our lives. I just wanted to make sure you understood that before we went any farther."

Adam rose slowly to his feet, still staring at the skull Joey had pushed around. The empty eye sockets stared back at him, hollow and dark, confirming Joey's warning.

"I understand," Adam said soberly as he reached for his lantern.

"Good," Joey replied. "Now let's get outta here. This place gives me the creeps."

After Christine's visit and map-guided tour of spacious New Eden, the North Side of Chicago seemed even more confining. It did not help that her back ached from sitting straight-shouldered on Adeline Forsythe's hard horsehair couch for over an hour and a half. Besides the occasional horsehair that poked through the gold-colored fabric to prick her back, she had also developed an itch on the back of her neck.

Slowly, she moved her head from left to right and back, hoping no one would notice her rubbing her neck against her high-necked blouse.

Trying to take her mind off the problem, she turned her attention back to the discussion. Though Mrs. Forsythe hosted the parlor meeting, Aunt Agnes moderated.

Every one of the eleven elegantly dressed women in the room came from Chicago's finest families. And everyone appeared to be an ardent follower of a new denomination or religious association called Christian Science.

Christine felt terribly out of place.

The first odd thing that distressed her happened right at the start of the meeting. One of the women stood up, propped her leg on a stool and hiked up her dress, right in plain view, to show how her leg had been healed!

Normally a most strict defender of good manners, Aunt Agnes

acted as if nothing out of the ordinary had occurred, but instead pointed at a location just above the woman's knee.

"For the past several months, our dear sister has lived with a dark knot on her leg. But as you can all plainly see, the knot is now gone. Restructuring her mental processes was the key, learning how to touch the Divine Mind."

Aunt Agnes had lifted and spread out her hands.

"As you all know, during a trip to Boston, I attended Mary Baker Glover's parlor meetings in the nearby city of Lynn. We are so fortunate, here in Chicago, to be privy to her wondrous revelation. Though now a small, determined band, we will one day be recognized as true pioneers of the Divine Science."

The second odd event happened during tea. One of the women announced that while eating a tea cake, she had received a vision from the Divine Mind. In her vision, she saw Mrs. Glover rising on a cloud above the Earth. Beams of healing light shone from her hands and feet.

For several minutes, Christine had sat utterly dumbfounded. Now, more bored than shocked, Christine tried to concentrate on what Aunt Agnes was saying, but found she could not.

Instead, her thoughts drifted back to her father's funeral. Then further back, to the days when his health still allowed him to preach. She thought about how different these women's beliefs were from what her father had taught.

Don't be an idle listener, but a doer of the word.

At that moment, another face superimposed itself over her father's: Simon Friend. Like her father, Simon was a doer, helping the dispossessed of Chicago rebuild their lives. Her father had worked with the Underground Railroad, helping slaves escape their cruel masters. Wasn't Simon's work after the Great Fire in Chicago also important?

She admitted that Simon acted a little peculiar, but far less so than the women sitting in this room!

At least, he was a practical man. Simon didn't just talk about progress, he had created an entire system of businesses to help those in need. He provided leadership and brought people together to work and to build.

And hadn't Aunt Agnes encouraged her to quickly find a job? Surely there could not be anything more proper and useful than being a teacher and helping the dispossessed. What were Aunt Agnes and her friends doing for the people of Chicago?

Christine glanced at her aunt and the circle of women around the room. Yes, she decided, Simon's ideals were closer to her heart than those of the women sitting here, including Aunt Agnes.

Christine remembered her tour of New Eden. She thought about the nice room Simon had reserved for her if she accepted the teacher's position. Though the room was not as large or elegant as her room in Aunt Agnes' house, it was clean and it did have a lovely view of a broad avenue lined with sugar maple trees. And the couple she would live with were nice, down-to-earth folks. The wife prepared meals for Simon and his admin istrative staff, and the husband had a position in New Eden's public works department. They both had made her feel sincerely welcome.

Christine smiled at last.

Monday morning she would accept the teaching position at New Eden.

Beneath a bright moon early Saturday morning, Lucius Morris turned away from the tall swirling column of flame and smoke crackling and flashing beyond the copse of trees beyond him. He crossed through the dry creek bed and with a sharp nod of his head, signaled his two deputies to follow.

Mounted on his horse, Simon Friend watched the fiery column reach higher and higher into the night sky. This particular warehouse had been mostly empty. Mostly.

Confidence rose in Simon. He took a deep breath of the night air. Now the lumberman would get the message.

Lucius loosened his horse's reins from a nearby bush, then slipped his foot into the stirrup and swung himself into the saddle. He turned up the collar to his dark wool overcoat.

"There'll be no evidence," Lucius explained with a sigh.

Simon turned his head slowly toward Lucius. Light from the fire over the trees cast a faint reddish gleam over the chief of security's face. Simon perceived regret in Lucius' eyes.

"We had no choice but to press the issue," Simon offered. "We need a lower price on the raw timber quote to complete our arrangements with Mr. McDonald."

Lucius nodded, reaching out and gently patting his horse's neck.

"Truly," Simon added more firmly, "you must put what happened at Peshtigo behind you. That was five years ago. What's done is done. It wasn't your fault that people died. I needed that lumber mill to be shut down."

Lucius' head snapped around, his eyes narrowed and his voice low, but sharp with emotion. "What do you know, Simon! I was in Peshtigo; you were in New Eden. You didn't strike the match that night! You didn't miscalculate what the wind would do. I did. And a town burned as the result and people lost their lives."

Simon waited for several seconds before replying. He looked up and found the other men still mounting their horses.

"I'll forgive your outburst, given our situation here. But you must learn to control yourself. Fortunately, your deputies did not hear you speak so directly to me."

Lucius looked away. His downcast eyes rose to the copse of trees, his face suddenly bathed in flickering oranges and reds. He shuddered.

Simon shook his head.

"Signal your men; our work is done."

***

Standing in the doorway to his office, Adam glanced at his pocket watch: 7 a.m.

He slipped the watch back into his vest, then stuffed his hands into his pants pockets. He frowned as he listened to his boss explain the battle plan for Monday's edition of *The Nation*.

A last-minute overhaul to Monday's issue would keep the entire staff working all Saturday and Sunday. Forget going home. Even the meals would be catered. And Monday afternoon, normally quiet, would be one pressure situation after another as they approached the magazine's 4 p.m. deadline.

He knew the disappointment showed on his face, just like it did with the rest of the staff.

Not only would that mean he would have to cancel his Monday morning meeting with Joey, but that he could not stop by and visit Christine until Tuesday.

He knew she would understand, but still, he wanted to share with her how his crime and corruption article was developing. Though she would be very concerned for his safety and well-being, he knew that she would support him, even pray for him. And he was sure she'd be interested in the possible criminal connections he and Joey had uncovered involving New Eden, the pretty little town that might not be as squeaky clean as it appeared to be.

Adam yanked his hands from his pockets and snapped to attention as his boss called out his name from across the room.

It was going to be a long, long weekend.

CHAPTER 10
SETTLING IN

"BOYS and girls, this is your new teacher, Miss Thompson. I am saddened, as you are, that Miss Wordsworth will not be returning. However, I expect you to show Miss Thompson the same respect and attention that you did for Miss Wordsworth."

With those remarks, Simon Friend, dressed in his familiar white suit and purple shirt, signaled Christine to stand behind the desk in front of the room. He smiled and waved to the class, then ushered the elderly substitute teacher from the room, closing the door behind them.

The schoolroom held thirty students in five rows of six desks each. Behind Christine to her left, a replica of the Ten Commandments in two tablets were attached to the wall. All twenty-six letters of the alphabet, in beautiful cursive, spanned the front of the room above the blackboard. On the wall above the door, a large clock read 11:15.

Her first task of the day would have her students memorizing Bible verses that she would write in white chalk along the top of the blackboard.

Christine felt comfortable teaching Blue School Number Two's third and fourth grade students. How different could this be from teaching Sunday school for over five years? If she needed help, Simon assured her other teachers would be more than willing to assist her in the evenings.

Gathering her thoughts, Christine glanced out the schoolroom window. Simon stood talking with his chief of security, if she remembered the bearded man's position correctly.

She stepped forward, wrapped her hands around the top rail on the back of the chair, and turned her attention to the class.

"Good morning students! Now, please take out your Bibles."

Lucius looked at Christine Thompson through the school room window as she spoke to the children.

"Yes, I'm sure. The name finally came back to me. I told you I never forget a face. I just didn't put the name and the face together when I passed her on the stairs last week."

"Surely you don't think that she and that Vestry character you told me about are working together somehow?" Simon asked, arching an eyebrow. "I would have sensed something in our interview. She does not hide her feelings well at all."

"Seeing Adam Vestry again was a big surprise." Lucius sighed and folded his arms over his clipboard and chest. "Vestry was acting pretty nervous. So was the man with him. Didn't even wait for their change. And I know Vestry placed me. The questions are, 'What was he doing in Slippery Ed's?' and 'Who was the man with him?' "

Simon lightly pinched his lips between his fingers.

"You'd better work on that. And keep an eye on little Miss Thompson there. If she becomes a problem, we'll whisk her right out of New Eden with slander against her character, just like we did Miss Wordsworth."

Lucius nodded as Simon turned and walked away.

Late Monday afternoon, Adam took a seat across from his boss's desk. The clock on the wall read 4:45 p.m. This week's edition of The Nation was already hitting the streets and the newsstands.

David Welch was of medium build with a clean-shaven ruddy face and wavy blond hair. His round spectacles reflected light from the window to his right as he leaned back in his swivel chair.

"So, Adam, where do we stand on our crime and corruption series?"

Adam leaned forward. "What do you know about a town called New Eden?"

"I know that the property where New Eden now stands used to belong to a man named Roy Benjamin. He ran one of the largest stockyards and slaughterhouses in Chicago. That was ten years ago. Now, it's an array of businesses that produce construction materials and supplies, from lumber to doorknobs. Got their own train stop. I hear it's run like a big corporation, but somehow with religious overtones. Pretty tight-lipped, too, and protective of their privacy."

David removed his spectacles and wiped them clean with his tie. "Think you're onto something?"

"I'd say I am." Adam grinned. "Your fellow Joey has proved invaluable."

"Joey's a good man who's had a run of bad luck."

"What do you mean?" Adam asked.

"It's up to him to tell you his story, not me."

Adam nodded. He knew his boss did not like to be pressed. "So, you say New Eden used to be a stockyard? That gives me a starting place, anyway, at City Hall."

"Land records?"

"Exactly," Adam replied, rising from his chair. "I'll go there first thing tomorrow morning. This evening I've got some personal business to attend to."

"Ah, the young woman you rode on the train with to Chicago. Lives on the North Side, with her aunt." A thin smile creased

David's face. He rubbed his eyes and slipped his spectacles back on. "You have a great eye for detail."

He looked up, but Adam was already out the door.

On the second floor of New Eden's Main Administration building, a group of nineteen men and women sat five abreast in four rows of wooden chairs. Twelve men were dressed in gray slacks and shirts. Seven others, two men and five women, unlike the twelve, wore shirts and blouses of varying colors. Some were green; others, tan and blue.

Lucius Morris stood at the front of the room, his clipboard on the table in front of him. A final straggler arrived just before the clock struck 5 p.m. The red-haired woman with a blue blouse quickly took her seat.

"I've called this special meeting of the People's Deputies to discuss the addition of four new undercover officers to our force," Lucius explained before introducing the two men and two women to the group.

"As you know, our undercover force is the key to maintaining a solid watch in the city's production areas. With the opening of our furniture factory and the glassworks division last month, we need to increase our policing levels. And with our new innovative kiln coming on line, be on the lookout for suspicious activity from visitors. No reporters or photographers are to be allowed near the kiln.

"As we announced last Friday, employee number 1465 has been removed from the central roster. We don't expect to see Miss Wordsworth back, but as a precaution she's now been added to our 'Not Welcome' list. Her photograph will be posted, with the others, at every security checkpoint by tomorrow morning.

"As always, I am counting on all of you to be alert. You are dismissed."

As the group cleared out through the double doors in the back of the meeting room, Lucius picked up his clipboard and opened the door to his office directly behind the podium.

Simon Friend tapped the folded telegram against his lips, then turned away from the special mirror inside Lucius' office.

He enjoyed watching the meetings unobserved and the sense of control the special mirror gave. He could hear what the deputies believed or felt without Lucius filtering the information, but they could not see him from the other side—as long as he kept the lamps turned low in Lucius' office. If the lamps were too bright, the special mirror would not work properly and the deputies would be able to see him watching from behind the mirror.

Lucius entered his office and took a seat behind his desk without acknowledging Simon's presence.

"Simple, concise and direct. I like the way you handle meetings," Simon said with a nod, ignoring Lucius' obvious silence. Simon knew that the memories of what happened five years ago in Peshtigo were still haunting Lucius, coming back to torment him.

Lucius put his pen aside and looked up. The sober expression on his face relaxed a little.

"Thank you."

"Something else," Simon added with a satisfied smile, unfolding the telegram he held in his hand. "We've just received word that our bid was accepted. Mr. McDonald was pleased. And he should be, given the amount of money we just made him.

"I took the liberty to deposit your portion of the profits into your account."

"Very well," Lucius shrugged, picking up his pen and turning his attention back to his paperwork.

Simon frowned. Lucius' conscience was his greatest weakness. But in a few days, Simon knew, Lucius' current moodiness would fade away. It always did.

A little time and a little money always seemed to do wonders for the human soul!

Adam straightened his tie and tugged at his vest, then brushed back the curl of hair from his forehead. He took a deep breath, then reached out and pulled the small brass knob that rang the doorbell. In the light of sunset, the brick front of Christine's aunt's house glowed with hints of red and orange. Lights in the right wing of the house, on both floors, gave Adam hope that Christine and her aunt were home.

Where else would they be on a Monday night, anyway?

A hand pushed a curtain aside in a narrow window to the right of the door. An apprehensive, oval face appeared. Adam noted white apron straps over a black dress.

Adam smiled and brought the box of chocolates into plain sight as the door opened.

"Yes, what can I do for you?" the blond-headed maid asked cautiously, looking Adam over.

"Hello, I'm Adam Vestry. Surely Christine has mentioned my name. I'm hoping that I can speak with her briefly."

The maid eyed the box of chocolates and smiled.

"I see. Well, I have unfortunate news. Christine is not here and neither is her aunt. She's off to the opera."

Adam grinned. "I didn't know that Christine liked opera. I'll have to remember that."

"I'm sorry. I was not referring to Christine. It's her aunt who's off to the opera," the maid explained in an apologizing tone.

Adam shifted his weight from one foot to the other. "I don't understand. I thought you said Christine wasn't here?"

"That is correct," the maid replied. Then she tipped her head slightly to the side, as if suddenly she understood the problem.

"Ah, you don't know, then. Christine no longer lives here with her aunt."

Adam felt the blood drain out of his face. "Not living here? Did something happen? Did she and her aunt—"

The maid shook her head vigorously. "No. She left her aunt on the very best of terms. Christine found herself a job, a teacher's position."

Still stunned, Adam was not sure if he should be upset or happy for her. He glanced at the box of candy, then back to the maid. "But why should she have left her aunt's so quickly? "

"Well, that's simple. New Eden's a good bit south of Chicago. Too far to travel every day. Anyway, her teaching position includes room and board. An all-around prudent move, so says her aunt."

Absentmindedly, Adam handed the maid the box of chocolates. He mumbled his thanks, turned and walked down the sidewalk toward the street.

When he got back to the boardinghouse, Adam slowly climbed the three flights of stairs to his room. Out of habit, he stepped to the window and pulled back the curtain, his eyes focusing on Christine's aunt's house a block away. Only then did he let the reality of what the maid had said finally sink in.

Christine had moved to New Eden!

An hour later, Adam plopped onto the empty bench seat opposite Joey. In contrast to Slippery Ed's smoky and open atmosphere, the patrons eating their appetizers and chef-prepared meals at the Golden Nugget ate in the privacy of high-backed booths.

Before Joey could even say hello, Adam spilled his story.

"I just can't believe it," Adam moaned softly. "What worse turn of events could have possibly happened?"

Joey dropped a lump of sugar into his coffee and stirred it, his eyes following the swirl of the spoon.

"A dozen worse turns could've happened," Joey replied at last, his voice low. "Christine's safe. And New Eden's not getting up and going anywhere. At least, you can find her."

Breathing deeply, Adam rested his arms on the table and folded his hands. The resignation in Joey's voice reminded Adam of his conversation earlier in the day with David, his boss. What had David said—Joey was a good man with a run of bad luck?

"You sound like you speak from experience," Adam said, shaking off his own concerns.

Joey lifted his spoon from his cup, then paused. He turned the spoon around, held it up and stared at it, as if he were looking at himself in a tiny mirror.

"Truth is," he began, spoon and eyes lowering, "I lost the only sweetheart I ever had. Back in '69, my printing business went bankrupt when my partner drained our bank account and ran off with the money. I was left with all the debts. Stupidest thing I ever did was when I took money from one of Mike McDonald's loan sharks to cover my company's debts."

The wall lamp above Joey's head cast shadows across his face.

"Well, after that, I was doing all kinds of small jobs for the shark. I knew I was wrong to do it, but I couldn't climb out the hole I'd dug for myself.

"Eventually, my fiancée discovered what I'd done. She was disgraced and ashamed. And rightly so. Next day, she broke off our engagement. The word spread quickly. All her family and her friends found out, too.

"Within the month, she left Chicago, for good. No one would even hint whether she'd headed east, south or west. Never heard from her since.

"Finally realizing how wrong I was, I begged and bought my way out of working for that shark. Cost me every last cent I owned, plus I was put on his blacklist. Any company associated with Mike McDonald's businesses in any way wouldn't so much as grant me an interview."

"I probably should have left Chicago a long time ago, myself." Joey looked up at last, his eyes moist and red. He stared Adam straight in the eye.

"So, yeah. I'd say a worse turn of events could've happened."

Twenty miles away, secure behind the locked iron gates and the high guarded walls of New Eden, Christine sat in front of her mirror.

She held up one of her five new, blue blouses to see what it would look like on her. The color accentuated her hair and eyes. She liked that.

She also liked her new room. It was perfect: modest, comfortable, and with a fireplace. She had the entire upstairs to herself. And on top of that, she lived in the Blue Sector. Though only her first day, she had already learned that not all living quarters were alike. Overall, the Blue Sector contained the nicest homes in New Eden.

And like other single women in New Eden, she lived with a family. The Andersons' house was like all the others on her street and for two blocks on either side, painted wood on the front, a steep roof, a brick chimney on one end, and two evenly spaced dormers. Mr. Anderson worked in the Main Administration building for the Chief of Public Works, who managed all of the Brown Shirts, as Mr. Anderson affectionately called himself. Mr. Anderson coordinated the community improvement projects and maintained the public areas and streets, including New Eden's three parks and baseball field.

Mrs. Anderson worked in the food service area. She reported to the Master Chef and aided in preparing the Executive Staff menus and meals. Most of the vegetables and meats eaten in New

Eden were grown or raised within the community itself. There were several hundred acres in the southeast corner of the grounds allotted to farming. Several large gardens provided an ample supply of fresh vegetables in the summer and canned vegetables in the other months. In addition, several hundred head of cattle grazed freely in fenced areas and provided a good supply of beef.

On the way home, Christine had also visited the community store. Everything she could ever need or want was there. A large variety of books and magazines, sewing supplies, even material for arts and crafts. As a teacher in the Blue Sector, she had freedom to leave New Eden on Saturday, as long as she was back in time for the weekly community worship service on Sunday.

Christine studied herself in the mirror. She felt good about where she was, about what she was doing with her life. New Eden was a great place to live, a place where people were treated fairly and equally, where everyone's talents and efforts really mattered. There were no class distinctions as in the outside world. And, in New Eden, both men and women were treated equally.

She smiled at herself and thought again about the color of her blouse. She did enjoy the immediate respect and deference that being in the Blue Sector gave her with other townspeople.

She thought back to that September afternoon less than two months ago at the Centennial Exposition and the white flag with the red letters spelling PROGRESS.

Christine rose from her chair, draped the blue blouse in front of her and pirouetted in front of the fireplace.

Progress was such a wonderful thing!

CHAPTER 11
SIMON MCGEE

At 9:45 A.M., Adam hurried down the stone steps to the basement of the Cook County Courthouse. He had visited several land record rooms before and knew it would not take him long to orient himself. There were over twenty rows of shelves and file cabinets with binder after binder of deeds and associated documents.

Fifty minutes later, Adam climbed once again onto a small stool in front of the tall shelves. He reached up and pulled down yet another large clothbound volume, this one titled Deed Book, Cook County, Illinois, January 1, 1871 to March 31, 1873. He carried it to a wooden table by the window and set it down next to his notepad and four other matching deed books.

Adam flipped through page after page after page. Another fruitless ten minutes passed. He arched his back and ran his fingers through his hair. If there was any information on Roy Benjamin's property to be found, he had no clue where to look next.

He shook his head in frustration and slumped forward in his chair, propping his elbows on the open deed book. A few moments later, Adam heard the soft scuffle of leather on wood approaching from behind. He turned in his seat.

An elderly gentleman shuffled toward him, dressed in a white cotton shirt, a bright red bow tie and pleated gray pants with a thin black belt showing at least four inches of slack. He was short, thin and silver-haired, with a weathered face. Oddly, he did not wear glasses, clearly revealing his most prominent features: thick, wiry eyebrows over pale-blue sparkling eyes.

"Hey there, sonny. Lookin' for somethin' in particular?" he asked, his voice high-pitched and cracking.

"Oh, I don't know," Adam shrugged, tapping his pencil on the blank notepad.

"Well now, that comment don't make a lotta sense. Why then are those books lyin' on the table?"

Adam grinned and chuckled. "A silly comment, I agree."

The old man extended an age-spotted hand. "Chester. Chester Roland's the name. Senior Records Clerk, City Hall."

Adam shook his hand. The firm grip surprised him. "Adam Vestry. I'm a writer for *The Nation*. I've been up and down your shelves for nearly an hour. I'm starting to think that the records I need were probably lost in the Great Fire."

The old man paused to scratch one of his bushy eyebrows. "If you're looking for a transaction from before the fire, you're likely right. But I know where we might find a reference or two about it."

Adam sat up straight in his chair. "What do you mean?"

Chester smiled. His teeth were crooked and chipped, but were mostly all there.

"I've been in Cook County since before it was a county. Been here since 1833, when Chicago was nothin' but a few log cabins in the marsh. I've seen this town grow from stockyards to a metropolis. Seen it burned to the ground and then built all over again.

"I used to know everything that went on in this town—births, marriages and land transactions—passed right through my hands in one form or another. Of course, after a time, I couldn't keep up with every baby and every piece of paper. By the time of the fire, there were nearly 60,000 buildings licensed in the city. But if it was something important, or controversial, I knew about it."

Chester pointed toward the back corner of the room. "Why don't you come to my office? Old Chester's got his own records, unofficial of course. Started compiling 'em right after the fire, when my wife died."

Adam picked up his notepad. "I'm sorry to hear about your wife."

Chester nodded, his pale-blue eyes misting suddenly. "I take comfort that she's in good hands."

Adam followed Chester to his office. The cubical-shaped office had space for a small desk, a bookshelf and three filing cabinets, but not much more. Chester pulled a chair from a table in the records area and placed it across the open doorway to his office, allowing Adam to sit halfway into the tiny, but neat room.

Chester grabbed one of two clothbound tomes from the bookshelf, then sat down. "Nearly all of the city records were lost. So, after the fire I started writin' everything down as I remembered it."

He touched a thin finger to his forehead and smiled.

"After eighty-two years, there's an awful lot of information stuffed in there! Now, what exactly are you lookin' for?"

Adam held back a grin and opened his notebook. Whether or not Chester could help him, he liked the spry old man. "I want to find out more about the old Benjamin property south of Chicago, now known as New Eden."

"Roy Benjamin," Chester softly tapped his finger against his forehead. "I knew Roy well, an honest man. He and his wife died a few months apart, just before the fire. But he'd already sold that property of his, back in '69. He sold it to . . . ."

Chester's thick eyebrows wrinkled up into a white, bushy line. He turned to his book and flipped back a third of the pages, then worked his way forward, page by page. After looking over twenty or so pages, he stopped. His finger traced down the page over the neat handwritten script, then paused for several seconds before tapping excitedly three times.

"To a man by the name of Simon McGee, out of Pennsylvania, from a little town called Paradise. Came to Chicago with a small fortune, or so the tabloids said. A strange fellow, I recall, with an imposing visage."

Chester looked up, his eyebrows still slightly scrunched together. "Now the name McGee reminds me of something else."

Paradise, the town where Christine's other aunt lived? Adam jotted down the information, then looked up. Chester's hand rested on the open book. His eyes darted back and forth in minute jumps, as he flipped through an even larger book inside his head.

"It's in here somewhere," Chester muttered, lightly tapping his forehead again. Suddenly, the tightness between his brows eased. He turned back to his book and began working forward, first by section, then by page. Shortly, his finger came to a stop.

"McGee. Hmm. Now I remember. Back in '70, he bought huge tracts of land northwest of Chicago, over fifty thousand acres. Bought it for a song and a dance, prime timberlands. Mostly hardwoods."

The crease between Chester's eyebrows returned. "Odd thing, come to think of it. Those timberlands have never been harvested. Not a single tree."

Adam made additional notes. "That means all the timber to rebuild Chicago after the fire came from somewhere else. Why not use cheaper, local timber? Why would McGee want to keep a stockpile?"

Chester shrugged his shoulders. "Even now, the West Side's built mostly with wood, like it was before the fire. The new immigrants movin' in still can't afford brick or stone."

Chester turned in his chair and looked Adam straight in the eye. Emotions flared behind his pale gaze. "Ever been to the West Side?"

Adam shook his head. "Not yet. Why?"

"It's just another firetrap! There're more shanties now than there were back in '71! All wood and tar paper!"

Adam blinked. Anger brightened Chester's cheeks. His eyes were staring off and searching again.

"Folks used to joke how there was a fire every Monday and Thursday in Chicago! But in '71, Chicago was a tinder box, waiting to explode. To fight the swamps and regular flooding, over 50 miles of pine-block streets and 600 miles of raised wooden sidewalks were laid down. Connected the North, East and West sides. Block after block of buildings and homes constructed of nothing but wood. Even the so-called fireproof buildings of brick and stone had wooden frames, floors and stairwells."

Chester's eyes started to bulge, his voice rising a notch.

"Doesn't matter whether it was O'Leary's cow or not that started the fire on October 8. Sooner or later it was bound to happen. All it took was one mistake. A watchman on top of the Courthouse signaled fire companies but sent them racing to the wrong location.

"When the fire alarm bells finally woke my wife and me, we jumped out of bed and looked out the second floor window. We didn't need our lamps. The room was glowing with bright crimson light. We just stood frozen at the window, our mouths wide open. The whole East Side of Chicago, from rooftop to rooftop as far as we could see it, was a storm-tossed sea of red-orange flame sweeping toward us."

Chester unlocked his trembling hands and grabbed his knees.

"My wife's mistake was trying to save the few keepsakes she owned, small things: a piece of jewelry, a photograph or two, a china teacup. All passed down from her grandmother. I begged her to leave it behind. I even tried pulling her by the arm, but she twisted free and shoved me hard in the chest.

"She ran from the kitchen back toward the parlor. For what last item I'll never know. I turned, yelling at the top of my lungs, then realizing I could not hear my own voice over the roar that filled my ears. My skin was tingling. The temperature in that room must've risen twenty degrees, like steppin' up to a blast furnace."

Chester's voice dropped suddenly to a whisper as he sagged forward in his chair.

"Next instant, my ears popped and I found myself struggling for breath. The hall by the parlor flashed from white to orange, followed by a writhing red spout of flame, thicker than a man, moving sideways and curling around the corner, then reaching toward the kitchen like the opening mouth of some giant snake!"

"I flung myself backward, crashing out the kitchen door, stumbling down the wooden steps into the side yard. I scrambled to my feet with the stench of scorched hair all over me.

"I turned toward the street, but a jagged, twenty-foot arm of flame surged out across the street, instantly igniting the front of the house across from ours. Through the roar, I heard a sudden cry of voices to my left. Families were screaming and pouring from their homes into the streets."

"In that moment I truly feared for my life. The yard behind me glared with brilliant reds. Heat buffeted my neck and face like a thousand fiery needles, singeing away more hair. I staggered forward, one foot splashing into what felt like iced water. Dazed, I looked down to find myself standing in the washtub my wife had left out from the day before.

"No time to think or to waste, I jerked up that tub and tipped it onto myself. The shock of the cold water splashin' and soakin' my housecoat and pajamas left me gasping as I tossed the tub aside and broke toward the street.

"I remember runnin', arms pumpin', with flames flashin' around me. A house on my left exploded into a shower of burning shingles. The blast knocked me forward, and I had to fight to keep my balance. Glowing cinders pelted my shoulders and danced around my feet. Above me, clouds of sparks and shingles spiraled high into the dark sky. Blazing kites of asphalt and tar paper the size of a roof careened on strong winds into the North Side of the city. I turned east at the next corner and found myself among a mass of terrified families running pell-mell toward Lake Michigan two blocks away."

Chester paused and looked at Adam. "At least that's the way I remembered it when I wrote it my journal.

"The tears I shed for my dear wife as I ran madly must've dried on my cheeks. And then somehow I was there with hundreds of others who stood with their backs to the lake, their faces aglow with the light of the Great Fire. Ragged for breath, I hardly noticed the ring of staring faces that formed around me.

"Finally, I saw a small boy standing with his sister. They were pointing at my shoulders and my feet. When I looked down, my housecoat fell off onto the sand. The housecoat was nothing more than a few strands of smoking cotton tatters. But even more amazing were my feet. The back half of my boots and my socks had been completely burned away. My heels and ankles were bare to the skin, and though scratched and bloody, showed no burns or blisters."

Chester opened a desk drawer and pulled out an old, black Bible. Adam watched silently as the fire dwindled in his eyes and voice.

"I have to believe God spared me that day for a purpose. Why, I can't be sure, but he did. And for the last five years, I've been warning folks that what happened once could happen again. But no one listens. Maybe next time it'll be the West Side, with all of those thousands and thousands of immigrants and other poor folks in their wooden shanties.

"And if it does, more than 300 people will die this time. It could be like Peshtigo, that little Wisconsin lumber town. Broke out with a fire of its own that very same October night. Two fires, same night. Peshtigo and Chicago. But the fire at Peshtigo hardly made the papers, even though every man, woman and child—over 2,000 people—died that night."

Adam did not say a word. His pencil lay still in his fingers. Though he felt a deep sympathy for Chester and all those who lost their lives in the fires, he could not shake the rising dread that crept over his skin like a dozen black spiders.

Adam stared at his notes. Paradise. New Eden. Two towns with the same name, once you took a moment to think about it.

Two towns. One old, one new, but both with one thing in common.

A man named Simon McGee.

CHAPTER 12

YOU WANT PROOF?

SIMON FRIEND climbed the wooden steps to the third floor of the Main Administration building, deep in thought. He crossed the wide landing, paused to look out the back window at the broad tree-lined avenue below, then continued down the hall to his private offices, his real office.

He despised his tiny second-floor office and reception room, but knew it was important to keep a humble profile when dealing with the public, both within New Eden and the outside world.

Using both hands, Simon flung open the double, solid mahogany doors that led into the main room of the suite. Standing on the threshold, he surveyed the Grand Room that took up over half the third floor.

Paintings of U.S. presidents from Washington to Grant lined the wall across from the doors to his ballroom-sized private office, with a sixteen-foot ceiling and three crystal chandeliers. On the wall to his right hung other paintings: fantastic landscapes of Yosemite and the wild west by Bierstadt and Moran, reproductions of Rembrandt's *The Binding of Samson* and a portrait of the ancient Babylonian king Nebuchadnezzar.

Simon entered the room at last, closing the doors behind him. The inside of the double doors merged suddenly as part of a thirty-foot, brightly painted panorama covering the entire wall, floor to ceiling.

Stopping in the center of the room, Simon spun around to face the dramatic panorama. His skin tingling, he lifted and opened his arms in a rush of excitement that stirred him to the core of his soul.

Simon beheld Chicago of the future, his Chicago, a future he would create. The panorama depicted what the city would look like fifty years from now if he had his way.

Simon's voice filled with pride. "You will not only be the Queen of the West, but you will be the Queen of America, the city of supreme progress!"

With delight, his eyes roamed over the painting of the city. Illumined by a golden sunrise, twenty blocks of stately buildings, some over fifty stories high, curved around the shoreline of Lake Michigan. The tiered buildings were majestic in their structural beauty and their never-before-conceived heights. To the north, west and south, the sunrise glimmered over planned communities, built on New Eden's pattern. Railroad tracks radiated outward from Chicago's business center by the lake, like spokes of some vast wheel. The gray bands of steel would bring commerce to every distant corner of the nation.

Sighing deeply, Simon pulled himself from his reverie and crossed the room toward his wide walnut desk.

Six high-back upholstered chairs were arranged in an arc in front of the desk. Behind the desk, custom-designed gas lamps bathed paintings in perfect cones of soft light. One of the largest and finest Persian rugs ever woven warmed the polished green marble floor.

In one corner, a crackling ruby fire in a double-sized marble fireplace, maintained by a People's Deputy twenty-four hours a day from November to April, heated the room. In the other corner, two large bubbling fish tanks teemed with exotic underwater flora and brilliantly colored fish.

Simon paused, his hands gripping the back of an upholstered

chair. He looked up at the larger than life-size oil painting. A portrait of himself. Depicted in his flowing white clerical robe, his likeness stood with his hands lifted upward and outward. The twelve gems on his replica of the Levitical breastplate, the Urim and the Thummim, shimmered with radiance of their own beyond the artistic beauty of the richly painted oils.

Simon's eyes sparkled. He stepped to the left of his desk and grabbed the right side of Nebuchadnezzar's portrait. The painting swung on an unseen hinge to reveal the round polished steel door of a wall safe.

He happily twirled the dial on the front of the safe: right, left, right. He swung the circular door open.

Simon removed a onyx treasure chest. His eyes bulged as he opened the ebon lid. He first counted the tight stacks of 1000-dollar bills. Then he removed a black velvet cloth rolled into a cylinder. He unrolled the cloth onto the center of his desk—the broad swathe of diamonds, rubies, emeralds and sapphires glittered against the velvet like stars on a dark night. He reached down, softly touching and counting each precious trove, his grin curling into a harsh smile.

He rerolled the velvet and gently placed the roll back inside the chest, then closed the smooth, dark lid and returned his treasures to the safe. With a flick of the wrist, he swung the safe shut, spun the dial, and then covered the safe with the portrait.

Simon walked to the fireplace. The fire's glow reddened his face as he stared into the pulsing coals.

Chicago's West Side, mostly untouched in the Great Fire, was an ever-growing and sprawling hodgepodge of poorly planned buildings and dingy wooden shanties.

Simon picked up two precisely split logs from the hearth and tossed them into the already hot fire. Bright orange sparks spiraled upward into the flue.

The West Side—filthy, ugly and populated with Chicago's

lowest classes, an ill-fated stain on the Queen of the West's beautiful new robe—would soon be cleansed away.

Cleansed away by fire!

As the train squealed to a stop at the New Eden Station, Adam rose from his seat. Through the window, he noticed several men and women in brown shirts and blouses busily weeding around the base of the trees in front of the long wall bordering New Eden. He exited the train and walked casually through the station.

Adam continued through the main entrance and up the cobbled pathway, pausing when he reached a rose-colored marble fountain. Small orange carp swam in the fountain's circular basin. To his right, he noticed a pathway leading through a stand of trees to a long row of warehouses situated at the far corner of the New Eden property. White smoke billowed from tapered brick smokestacks. The buildings situated closest to the tracks had loading docks with boxcars and flatbeds parked in front of them.

Adam's eyes turned to three flatbed rail cars loaded high with logs. He wondered where McGee was getting his timber. Adam also wondered how Lucius Morris fit into McGee's scheme of things. But most of all, he thought about finding Christine. It was too late to worry about Lucius identifying him. Connections to Mike McDonald or not, Adam knew he had to get Christine out of here. And, if he carefully watched his step, he might be able to get the answers he needed before trouble erupted.

A tap on his shoulder caused Adam to turn around. He found himself facing a blond-haired man wearing a gray shirt and black trousers.

"Excuse me, sir. Do you have a pass?"

"I didn't know a pass was needed." Introducing himself, Adam gave his reason for being there.

The deputy's countenance hardened noticeably. "You write

for a magazine, eh? In that case, you'll need to speak with our executive manager, Mr. Simon Friend."

Simon Friend sat behind the small desk in his second-floor office and contemplated his mastery of people and circumstances. As he did, Henry, his elderly secretary, poked his head through the doorway.

"Mr. Friend, there's an Adam Vestry here to see you. He says he works for a magazine and wants to write an article about New Eden."

Simon bolted straight up in his chair. "Adam Vestry! Are you sure of the name?"

Roy nodded.

Simon folded his hands and pursed his lips. Why would Adam Vestry suddenly show up in New Eden? Ultimately, there was only one way to find out!

"Send him in, Henry. I'll talk to him."

Adam Vestry entered the office. Simon shook the dark-haired young man's hand and offered him a seat. Adam explained how he was a feature writer for *The Nation*, how he was researching a new series on innovation and progress, and how the magazine wanted New Eden as the centerpiece for the series.

Simon nodded, but refused to let himself be fooled into thinking Adam was here to write a story about progress. No, the promise of an article was merely a ruse, a sly attempt by Adam to gain free movement around New Eden. But for what? Why did the magazine have such an interest in New Eden?

Simon felt a sudden tightness in his stomach. Was it the burning of the lumberyard? Had Adam made connections after spotting Lucius at the tavern with Michael McDonald's accountant?

Maybe Lucius had been right after all about Christine

Thompson.

Collecting his thoughts, Simon stood up from his desk and extended his hand. "Vestry, I think it's a great idea. I want you to have full access to the grounds—our factories, our rail system, everything. We're even getting ready to unveil an innovative ceramic process, with patents pending."

Simon smiled. "Investigate whatever you want. Talk to anyone."

He watched a faint line of anxiety begin to ripple across Adam's face, then vanish abruptly into a smile.

Adam shook Simon's hand. He was surprised by the force of Simon's grip, but kept his composure. "Thanks so much. What's my next step? Will this pass get me around everywhere?"

Simon nodded. "I'll handle the necessary details and make sure everyone knows who you are and exactly why you're here. All I ask is that you allow me to review the article before you submit it, to check for any inaccuracies. We wouldn't want your readers to be misled."

"Absolutely," Adam concurred, flexing the fingers of his right hand. "How about if I come back next week. Say, Tuesday, to go over a draft of the article with you?"

Simon looked at his calendar. "Excellent. Let's make it three o'clock."

Adam nodded. "Three o'clock it'll be."

Christine Thompson stood in front of her class and leaned back against her wooden desk. Even though this was only her second day teaching, she already felt comfortable with her class.

"Thank you for an excellent reading, Susan," she said to the eight-year-old with black curly hair in the front row. "Jimmy, it's your turn to read. Two pages, please."

Jimmy shifted in his seat, shot no one in particular a big frown, then slowly began to read.

Christine looked out her window and nearly dropped the book she was holding. To her complete surprise, she saw Adam Vestry heading up the sidewalk to her schoolhouse.

Christine held up her hand. "Jimmy, please stop."

Jimmy and the rest of the class looked up from their books.

"I want everybody to read silently to themselves to the end of the chapter," Christine said, smiling. "I'll be right outside."

She quickly closed her reader, placed it on the desk and opened the schoolhouse door. Adam stopped halfway up the steps. She saw both happiness and concern in his face.

"I'm so sorry I didn't get word to you about my new job," Christine explained as she closed the door behind her. From the heat in her cheeks, she knew embarrassment showed on her face.

Adam forced a grin. "I had no idea there were so many schoolhouses in New Eden. I've spent at least a half hour trying to find you."

Christine did not understand. "Why didn't you just ask for me? I'm listed in the roster at the Main Administration building. This is Schoolhouse Number Two, Blue Sector."

Adam nodded. "I didn't want it to look like I was singling you out. Mr. Simon . . . Friend thinks I'm here to write a feature story about progress and such."

Even more confused, Christine came down a step closer to Adam. "I'm not sure what you mean. If I remember, you're supposed to be working on a crime series."

"I am," Adam said, swallowing hard. "And right now, New Eden is a major part of it."

Stunned, Christine folded her hands. "Did you tell Simon you're an investigative reporter?"

"Well, I couldn't exactly be direct with him, could I, if what I'm telling you is true? Besides, I had to see you, to get you and to take you back to your aunt's."

Christine's cheeks grew hot, but not from embarrassment.

"Mr. Adam Vestry, you're not just prying—you're spying! And your fear that I'm in some kind of danger, why that's the craziest thing I've ever heard! There's not an unhappy soul anywhere in New Eden."

Christine leveled her gaze. "Do you have any proof?"

Now it was Adam who looked stunned. "What do you mean, proof?"

"Evidence. Confirmation." Christine's eyes flashed.

"No, I suppose I don't. Not yet anyway." Adam squared his shoulders. "But I will."

Christine glanced over her shoulder back toward the class. She could see every one of the students, their heads bobbing up and down and peering over the tops of their books out the windows.

"Adam, I've got a classroom of anxious students to tend to."

"Christine, wait." Adam reached out and gently put his hand on her arm. "I'm sorry for storming up to the schoolhouse and acting like a gangbuster. I truly am. But we should talk. You need to hear what I have to say."

Breathing slowly to regain her composure, Christine considered Adam's words.

"Sunday afternoon, here in New Eden. Since you have a pass, why not attend our weekly worship service? It will fit in nicely with your cover about writing an article. We can talk afterwards."

Adam's shoulders drooped. "That's four days from now!"

"That's my offer," Christine said sharply, stepping back inside the schoolhouse. "Now, I have a job to do!"

As she closed the door, she saw Adam angrily drive one fist into his other palm, frustration creasing his face as he squeezed his eyes shut.

Though she walked straight and steady from the door to her desk, a series of tremors slowly worked their way down her shoulders and back. Though she could not gauge the truth of his charges, she could judge the strength of his belief in them.

Hands shaking slightly, Christine picked up her reader and tried to focus her attention on the lesson.

Simon detailed his conversation with Lucius Morris who shifted uneasily in his chair.

"I remember Adam," Lucius commented after Simon was finished, "as a very nosy sort of fellow. His father was a newspaperman, so snooping around is in his blood. Keeping up with him will be tough. My deputies are stretched thin as it is."

Simon stared through the one-way mirror into the now-empty meeting room, his hands behind his back. "No excuses. I want two plainclothes deputies following him at all times. Inside or outside of New Eden. Set up shifts. Shuffle duty schedules. Do whatever you have to do. I want to know what he's up to."

"Should I assign someone to keep an eye on Christine?" Lucius asked. "Someone who won't raise suspicion."

Simon looked over his shoulder. "An excellent precaution. See to it immediately. Do you have someone in mind?"

Lucius studied the duty roster. "I've got someone who'll do."

"Good. I can't have Vestry creating trouble now," Simon said, turning back to face the window. A jolt of excitement ran up his arms as he considered his decision to cleanse Chicago of the filthy West Side.

But telling Lucius was another thing. would not be able to bear it. But the time would come soon enough, when Lucius would no longer have a choice in the matter.

A faint reflection on the back of the mirrored glass showed Lucius sitting at his desk, head lowered and making notations on his clipboard.

His sensitive conscience from his mistake at Peshtigo would one day be his undoing.

Simon frowned bitterly, then pressed his lips into a thin, bloodless line.

Christine left the Blue Sector Community Dining Hall and casually strolled back home toward the Andersons'. She breathed deeply of the cool night air. Calm and peaceful, New Eden's Blue Sector looked beautiful at night. Straight, neat rows of gas lights illumined the cobblestone streets. Lamp and fire light glowed in the windows of buildings and houses stretching all the way to the western edge of the wall.

New Eden, the words formed silently on her lips, a single-minded community of hard-working, sharing people. She thought briefly about her conversation with Adam. Again, she saw him slam his fist into his palm and the painful look on his face.

Christine stuffed her hands into her coat and kept walking.

At first she'd been so happy to see him, but then, he began blustering about including New Eden in his articles on crime! How could he possibly think such a thing?

Still, she felt badly about the way she had abruptly closed the school door in his face. On Sunday, she would apologize to him.

Christine looked upward. Stars twinkled brightly in a thick band across the night sky. And directly above her hung a full moon, blazing and seemingly alive, its dark, eerie spots forming features of a misshapen face that stared down at her.

She shuttered and drew her shawl more tightly around her, then quickened her pace and headed home.

"Christine wants proof," Adam exclaimed while kicking an iron bolt and watching it skitter over the rough pine blocks of the raised street. "And proof's the one thing we don't yet have!"

Light from a bright moon bathed the back street and nearby

Chicago River that separated the East and West sides.

Hands buried in his heavy coat, Joey nodded understandingly behind an upturned collar.

"I'm making progress, but it's slow-going. I've got to keep my normal low profile. Folks all over the city see me come and go every day—running errands, delivering packages, rushing telegrams. I stop, we chat. Cabbies, shop owners, bartenders. But if I ask too many questions, they'll get suspicious."

Adam nodded in return, then reached down and picked up the bolt he had kicked moments before.

"I know. Simon McGee, Simon Friend, whoever he is, is crafty—and cocky. I got the distinct feeling that he was playing word games with me today, poking and jabbing and laying traps to see if I would stumble somehow. Then, with a big smile on his face, he tried to crush my hand—like some schoolyard bully!"

"Maybe we're getting closer than we think," Joey said with a cheerful lilt in his voice. "Though I have to admit, your latest idea is pretty hard to accept. Aren't you stretching this McGee forest-thing a bit too far? So what if he's never harvested any trees? Do you really think that Friend might start another fire in Chicago just so he can supply the wood to build it up again?"

Adam tossed the iron bolt into the air, then quickly snatched it with one hand. "Funny you say that. I was reading my Bible the other night and, for no special reason, I stopped flipping pages and ended up in the book of Ecclesiastes. I came across some scriptures, starting in chapter three, verse one, that sent chills running up and down my spine.

"It goes something like this, 'To every thing there is a season, and a time to every purpose under heaven. A time to be born, and a time to die. A time to plant, and a time to pluck that which is planted. A time to kill, and a time to heal. A time to break down, and a time to build up.' "

Adam turned to face Joey, his voice rueful. "Somehow, don't

ask me why, but I just believe that something terrible is about to happen, something that shouldn't happen. Something that's not at all a part of God's providence for Chicago.

"I just hope that come Sunday, I have evidence Christine will accept. All I have right now is the fact that Lucius Morris met a corrupt politician and a criminal accountant at a seedy bar. I can also make a case that Simon McGee is Simon Friend, though changing one's name is hardly a crime."

Joey crossed his arms over his chest, then looked across the river to the irregular patchwork of yellow lamplight shining from thousands of windows.

"I leave understanding the Bible to you. What I still can't believe is that Mike McDonald wants to torch the West Side. He's got dozens of well-disguised gambling rooms and a number of legitimate businesses over there."

Joey rocked back and forth on his feet. "Besides checking out those warehouse fires you mentioned, I'll visit a few taverns and pool joints on the West Side. If McDonald authorized something like this, somebody somewhere should have noticed if any of Mike's boys have been preparing for a quick exit. Just don't set your hopes on me showing up in the next few days with rock-solid proof."

"Maybe you're right. If I'm wrong, all I've done is endangered our lives by poking around a little too much where I shouldn't have," Adam reasoned in a half-serious, half-joking manner while watching Joey's eyes pop open in surprise.

"But if I'm right about McGee and what he's planning to do, thousands of people and their homes and businesses could be facing another disaster."

Joey turned suddenly to face Adam. In the moonlight, Adam saw fear ripple over Joey's face as his friend spoke.

"If you're right, then I'd say we're in even deeper trouble. Big-time trouble. We could find ourselves wearing a brand new pair of cement shoes and taking a midnight swim."

Adam followed Joey's gaze as he turned to stare into the dark, slow-moving waters of the Chicago River where many an unfortunate man had disappeared.

"We'll just have to trust God with that," Adam replied, reaching back, then flinging the iron bolt far into the river.

Standing quietly side by side, they both heard a sharp plop as the bolt struck the water and sank somewhere in the darkness.

CHAPTER 13

GIVE THE MAN SOME ROPE

CHRISTINE carried the last of the messy plates and bowls to the deep sink and plopped them into the hot soapy water.

With the sleeves of her blue blouse rolled up to the elbows, Christine vigorously scrubbed away the last sticky remnants of Saturday night's dinner.

Her new friend and roommate, Kate Warner, a tall, full-figured woman with long, dark hair, brown eyes and a dark complexion, worked beside her. She also wore a blue blouse with the sleeves rolled up. Reaching upwards, Kate hung a freshly cleaned copper pot on a rack suspended from the ceiling.

Further down the line of sinks, brown- and tan-bloused women performed similar tasks.

"I think it's marvelous to serve in the community kitchen like this once a week," Christine said to Kate.

Kate placed her hands on her hips and smiled at Christine. "Simon says that serving helps us all remember we're equal, even though we wear different-colored shirts. It helps us to remember that we're all just ordinary people."

Christine thought carefully about Kate's comments. Ordinary people. Simon had a way of explaining things that made so much sense. Wasn't this the way the world was supposed to function, people working side by side, sharing equally in chores and responsibilities for the common good of others? Yes, Simon had discovered a way to mold all aspects of a person's life into a meaningful whole.

And tomorrow morning, she'd attend her first weekly worship meeting. Adam would be there, too, and they would finally have time to talk. She had seen him in passing twice over the past three days, speaking with various Sector managers and touring the grounds. He appeared to be writing an article. Hopefully, after they discussed things in a calm and straightforward manner, she could put his suspicions about New Eden to rest.

She dried her last pot, rolled down her sleeves and grabbed her coat. Kate joined her at the door.

Christine knew she still had one last chore before she and Kate went to their evening lecture.

"I've got to take my dirty clothes to the laundry."

"I hope the stains come out," Kate said with a small frown, glancing at the front of her blouse.

"Doesn't matter," Kate replied cheerfully. "If the laundry can't clean it, you'll get a brand-new one."

Christine smiled and slipped on her coat.

Adam couldn't be more wrong about New Eden!

"I've read Kate's reports carefully," Lucius explained, leaning back in his office chair, "Christine and Adam were long-time friends back in Philadelphia. After Adam's father was murdered, Adam went to New York and worked for a newspaper there as an investigative reporter for four years. Then he got a job here in Chicago. Christine met him unexpectedly on the train to Chicago. He stills cares about her."

Simon pursed his lips and tightened his eyebrows. "So, you don't think they're working as a team to spy on us then?"

Lucius shrugged. "Kate doesn't believe that Christine's told her everything, but they've only been roommates for three days. It's only a matter of time before she confides completely in Kate."

"But I did follow up on Vestry." Lucius flipped a page on his clipboard. "He does work for *The Nation*. Started last week. Couldn't verify his claim about the article he told you he's writing. But, after reviewing the deputies' reports, Vestry seems to be doing just what he said, collecting information for an article. All of the Sector managers said he seemed real natural; he didn't pry around, ask nosy questions or make negative statements about you or New Eden.

"And finally, he's staying at a boardinghouse a block away from where Christine's relative lives. That supports Kate's belief in his romantic interest in Christine."

Simon leaned his back against the wall with the one-way mirror.

"Something's still not right. I can feel it. Vestry started to squirm when I told him to 'investigate' whatever he wanted. He recovered nicely, but not before he gave away his hand."

"Maybe we shouldn't let him into the Sunday meeting?" Lucius asked. "Normally, we don't allow outsiders to attend."

"We can't jeopardize Christine's trust in Kate. Christine told her that Adam was planning to visit on Sunday. No, we'll let him in.

"Just make sure your plainclothes deputies carefully track Vestry and Christine wherever they go. I want to know how much time they spend together and, as much as possible, what they talk about."

Simon smiled, his eyes narrowing.

"Let's give the young man some more rope to play with. Maybe we'll get lucky and he'll hang himself."

Back in Chicago, Adam stared out his boardinghouse room window and ran his fingers through his hair, then yawned. To no avail, he tried to rub the weariness from his eyes and face.

Now, at ten-thirty, the windows of Spinster Thompson's house were nothing more than black splotches in the darkness. Adam wondered if the old lady and her maid enjoyed living alone.

Adam turned from the window and looked over the many sheets of paper scattered on his desk. Saturday had been another long day, after spending most of Thursday and Friday carefully snooping around at New Eden. He had retraced his steps, revisited every conversation, and reconsidered every observation as he tried to find any clue that would support his suspicions about Simon McGee.

But as hard as he tried, he could not find a single piece of damaging evidence. And without evidence, Christine could not be convinced to leave.

Adam plopped down on the end of his bed. Still, his two and a half days in New Eden had not been totally worthless. For the last six hours, he had counted the number of manufacturing plants, mills, artisan shops, farm acreage and head of livestock he had seen. Then he had calculated an estimate of New Eden's yearly sales to outsiders. The numbers staggered him. Even if his computations were only fifty percent accurate, McGee ran a multifaceted business grossing ten million dollars a year—an operation that could funnel millions in profits back into the pockets of crime boss Mike McDonald and his organization.

No, New Eden was not the wonderful town Christine thought it to be. New Eden was full of hard-working people who gave themselves to the idea of progressive utopianism—happily going about their daily lives, offering their labor for special paper money that could only be spent in New Eden's shops for small luxuries or books from an approved reading list.

Life at New Eden was no different than life in the factories and sweatshops.

The result—even greater profits for Simon McGee and Mike McDonald to share.

Adam reached across his bed to the nightstand and grabbed the book he'd purchased with real U.S. greenbacks at New Eden's company store. He turned the book over in his hand and glanced at the title.

Das Kapital. Adam frowned. He had started reading the book earlier. Karl Marx, a German writer and thinker, was sharply opposed to everything Adam believed about the American way of economics, government and religion. And Marx's godless view of life stood in direct opposition to the Bible.

With an exhausted sigh, Adam pushed himself back onto the bed. He fluffed his pillows and stuck them behind his back. He returned *Das Kapital* to the nightstand and picked up his Bible.

He paused for a moment before opening it, realizing that he had not seen Joey for nearly three days. And Joey had not left any messages at the front desk.

Adam opened his Bible for his daily reading.

Still, even if he couldn't find the physical evidence he needed to shake Christine's trust in Simon McGee, a.k.a. Simon Friend, maybe he could change her mind another way.

He closed his eyes and prayed.

CHAPTER 14
THE MEETING OF THE PEOPLE

A hush fell over the congregation. Faces young and old looked up expectantly across the 3,000-seat People's Meeting Place, an expansive hexagon built of oak, cedar and mahogany located in the center of New Eden.

Christine Thompson stood proudly on the raised platform in the center of the hall. Standing beside her on the rich purple carpet were nine other new members of the New Eden community. And in front of the ten of them, Simon Friend.

Wooden beams as thick as a man's torso arched upward from each of the six corners and converged some fifty feet above the floor. Between the beams, long rectangular glass skylights lit the hall. Long rows of pews wrapped around the platform on all six sides. Six purple carpeted aisles radiated from the platform like spokes on a wheel, each leading to one of six double doors. Christine basked in the enjoyment of seeing so many happy faces and the harmonious bands of colors surrounding the platform. In the rows closest to the platform, men and women wore white shirts or blouses; in the next three rows, blue; then, greens, tans and browns. And the Grays, as everyone called them, stood or sat to the right and left of each door.

Christine's eyes followed the purple aisle cutting through the rings of color all the way to the doors at the back of the building.

She suppressed a smile as Adam slipped in just before the doors closed and took a seat in the visitor pews along the back wall.

Simon nodded at Christine, and she stepped forward.

"As we begin our weekly Meeting of the People, I want to welcome our new members. First on the list is Christine Thompson, our new third and fourth grade teacher in Blue School Number Two. Please greet her after the meeting."

Simon held one hand, palm down, above her head. "Welcome, daughter."

With a gentle wave of his arm, Simon dismissed Christine. As Simon signaled the next new member to stand before him, Christine took her seat beside Kate in the pews designated for the Blue Sector.

One by one, Simon introduced and blessed each new member, then stepped forward to the edge of the platform.

Simon raised his arms upward in a large V. "Let's all stand and join our voices together in singing The Centennial Hymn, written by the prophet of progress John Greenleaf Whittier."

As the large pipe organ blasted out the first lines of the refrain, Simon waved his arms and the entire assembly rose to their feet.

Christine felt someone bump her right arm. Turning, she found herself looking into the smiling face of Adam Vestry.

Christine was taken aback. Folding her hands in front of her, she leaned and put her mouth near his ear.

"These rows are reserved for members who work in the Blue Sector. The visitor seats are in the back."

Adam's gaze narrowed slightly. He kept his voice low enough that he would not be heard over the singing. "Yes, I noticed the unique color-matching system. I just wanted to sit next to you. Didn't realize it was a crime to sit in the wrong pew."

He fingered the new blue shirt beneath his tie and gray vest. He smiled, "I did try to coordinate colors the best I could!"

Christine wanted to reply, but the hymn came to a close and the room grew quiet once again. They sat down.

Simon stepped to the edge of the platform. He removed a white fold of cloth draped over his shoulders and chest, revealing a jewel-encrusted breastplate atop his flowing white robe.

The breastplate, an exact replica of the Levitical Urim and Thummim, hung from his neck with two wide chains of gold interwoven with blue, purple and scarlet linen. Covering the breastplate were twelve large dazzling gemstones.

Simon's breastplate and white robe glowed in the long shafts of light streaming down from above. He looked slowly from side to side, waiting until the room grew completely still.

"Brothers and sisters of New Eden, this is another glorious day in Paradise. Today we have welcomed ten new members.

"But as nature itself reveals, growth is a slow process. Time is needed for people to abandon their old and tiresome traditions. One needs eyes of faith to see our evolution from glory to glory. Once, we were but tiny organisms in a great sea, but now we are men and women building beautiful cities and great machines of iron and steel. To mortals, this process appears to have taken millions of years, but to God, only days. Yes! How grand and glorious our future shall be! Can one imagine it? And yet I say, standing before you today, we are progressing."

Christine felt Adam's gaze turn to her, but she kept her eyes fixed on Simon as he slowly turned and spoke to members facing each side of the hexagonal platform.

"I am reminded of the once-heroic Mill Girls of Lowell, Massachusetts. Twenty-five hundred hard-working young ladies, dressed in white with blue sashes and parasols, marching two abreast to their daily tasks at the cotton mill. Those rural farm girls, housed in dormitories built by the managers of Lowell, were the first fruits of a new generation and century.

"Francis Lowell, conceiver and builder of this marvelous town, died in 1811. Within fifty short years, this worker's paradise was gone and the wondrous town of Lowell deteriorated into a common and dirty little mill town.

"And why? Because the mind of man was not prepared to embrace equity and fairness. Lowell and other communities like it have sprung up, only to shortly die. Need I remind you of New Economy, of Oneida, of New Harmony?"

Simon continued to turn and once again faced the side of the room where Christine sat.

He reached down to the edge of the platform, picked up a large Bible and opened it. He gazed out at the congregation, his head moving slowly from left to right.

"'And I, John, saw the Holy City, a New Jerusalem, coming down from God out of heaven, prepared as a bride adorned for her husband.' Brothers and sisters, we are that New Jerusalem. The worship we offer is the work of our collective hands. Our temples are the factories where our sacrifices are made. Our city walls are built of living stones which are our very lives, bonded together in the spirit of community."

Christine sensed Adam shifting in his seat, but forced herself to ignore him.

Simon stood very still. "Our future is bright. We are on a course that no man can turn back, for upon our shoulders weighs the burden of rebuilding Chicago, the only true Queen of Progress and the Future."

Simon slowly spun around in a complete circle, repeatedly thrusting his arm and pointing into the hushed crowd.

"Hold fast! Be strong! In the days ahead, we will need fresh resolve and renewed dedication. As Jesus taught, any branch that doesn't bear fruit must be cast into the fire and burned. The Apostle Paul, did he not warn that when one builds with wood, hay and stubble, it shall be cleansed by fire, and the fire shall try every man's work! And cities take heed—even Sodom and Gomorrah could not escape the fireballs of judgment thrown down from Heaven!"

Following Simon's fiery message, The Meeting of the People continued with handing out gold pins for those who excelled in community service, taking an offering, making announcements, and singing a hymn.

As the hymn drew to a close, Simon Friend opened both arms.

"May peace be with you, my brothers and sisters. As you go about your recreational activities today, find rest and be kind to one another in the spirit of equality."

The organ blasted out a recessional tune and people slowly filed out into the aisles. Christine introduced Adam to Kate, and after a brief conversation about when she would be home, the two women exchanged pleasantries and parted.

When Christine and Adam reached the aisle, she looked up and, for a second, caught the gaze of Lucius Morris, Chief of the People's Deputies, standing by the platform.

Then, as if Lucius had not been looking at her at all, he turned to Simon who now knelt at the edge of the stage.

Christine felt a gentle hand on her arm and turned around.

Adam offered her a concerned smile. His eyes and brow seemed weighed down with an unseen burden. Christine's heart softened. She reached up and brushed a curl of hair from his forehead.

"You've been so very patient," she said softly, forcing her own smile. "Let's go get a bite to eat and talk."

As Adam followed Christine out the double doors, he glanced over his shoulder back into the huge six-sided meeting room.

He shuddered. His emotions boiled with a mix of amusement, sadness and fear. Some of McGee's comments had been almost laughable, except that no one had laughed! How could anyone accept his mishmash of philosophy and misquoted Scripture? But most of all, his references to Sodom and Gomorrah and to fireballs of judgment only reinforced Adam's growing conviction that Simon planned to burn down Chicago's West Side.

Christine stopped and turned around, smiling, her strawberry-blonde hair shimmering in the full sunlight. The warmth of the meeting hall had left a touch of pink in her cheeks. The mild temperatures and the rich blue sky made their spirits soar.

Everyone's but mine, Adam thought to himself. He fought down his rising emotions. Alarming Christine with his true feelings would complicate the already-troublesome situation.

Christine led Adam across the grounds through knots of families and small groups talking and enjoying the pleasant afternoon. They strolled across a small wooden footbridge that spanned the S-shaped bend of a creek.

The footbridge led to a wide-open field where New Eden's eight-team baseball league played its games. On Sunday, a row of temporary booths behind the webbed backstop served picnic foods of all kinds, along with drinks and desserts. Already, the bleachers behind first and third bases were starting to fill with hungry men, women and children loaded down with sliced meats, thick slabs of yellow and white cheeses, polished apples, a variety of pickles and fresh, warm breads.

For a moment, Adam was lost in the superb smells and flavors of his free meal. Sitting beside Christine on the bleachers directly behind third base, he enjoyed the cloudless sky and bright sun that warmed his face.

But Adam knew this idyllic setting worked against his reason for being in New Eden. He had not come to eat, drink and share Sunday festivities with Christine. His conscience stricken, he set the stiff white paper that held the last morsels of his turkey sandwich on the painted wooden bleacher beside him.

But when he looked up, Christine was already poised to speak.

"Adam," she began optimistically, "I hope this visit today has opened your eyes to what New Eden is really about. I've so much wanted you to see just how happy and fulfilled I am, and the others here, too. Simon is right when he calls New Eden a worker's paradise."

Christine paused and wrapped her hands tightly around her soda. Adam saw from the shifting expression on her face that she had finally perceived his distress.

"You're angry at me," she said with a hurt look.

Adam breathed in slowly. "No. I'm not angry at you, Christine. But I came here today with even stronger concern than when we spoke outside your schoolroom the other day."

Now it was Adam's turn to watch Christine's face darken. She closed her eyes and her lips tightened into a line.

"I don't have the rock-solid proof that you want. But I do have circumstantial evidence linking Simon and New Eden to a man named Mike McDonald, the most influential crime boss in Chicago, and to a corrupt official in the mayor's office.

"But that's not all. I believe that I can also show that Simon Friend is actually Simon—"

Christine cut Adam off in mid-sentence. Her voice trembling with exasperation. "Adam! I don't want to hear it!"

Christine's eyes flashed with indignation.

"What better proof can I give you of our innocence than what you can see with your own eyes! Look around! Do you see any unhappy faces? Do you see any hunger? Do you see any children with improper shoes or clothing? There're no pickpockets here, Adam. No alleys littered with rotting garbage. No beggars pressing their open hats in your face."

Adam raised his hands as if to ward off an attacker. "Christine! Please don't turn this conversation into a battlefield. You agreed to meet today, remember, so that I could share with you my on-going investigation.

"You talk and act like I'm accusing you, but I'm not. You must believe me. You, of all people, know how I have a nose for trouble—finding and getting into it! Listen to me—Simon Friend is not the man you think he is. He has a history that goes back to Paradise, where your Aunt Mildred lives. And your chief of security, don't you know who he is? He's the man my father—"

For the second time, Christine cut Adam off, reaching out and pressing her warm hand over his mouth. Long waves of strawberry blonde hair framed her suddenly anguished face. Tears welled in the corners of her eyes.

"I don't think I can bear another word, Adam. You refuse to let yourself see the goodness all around you. Maybe you don't want to see it.

"But I can't let you ruin this wonderful opportunity," she said, her lips quivering. "I love New Eden. I love being a teacher. I love my home and I love the people here, like the Andersons and my new friend Kate."

Christine leaned forward, her eyes pleading as she slowly pulled her hand away from his mouth.

"Don't you see, I'm finally making my own way. Can't you accept that? I need your support, not reproof."

Adam reached up and gently dabbed the tears from her cheeks with his handkerchief. He watched agonizingly as a soft smile began to form on her face.

"I'm more sorry than you can imagine, Christine."

Pain clouded his eyes. The words stalled in his mouth and they tasted bitter, like medicine.

But Adam did not hold what he had to say.

"I won't give up. I can't give up until I've rooted out the truth about New Eden and Simon Friend."

Christine sat very still, her blue-green eyes dry and pale. She played with the tips of her long strawberry-blonde hair, wrapped behind her head and down over one shoulder.

Christine turned her head and stared across the baseball diamond at the crowded bleachers on the other side. Though the afternoon sun warmed Adam's face, her reply struck him like a blast of arctic air.

"Then there's nothing more to say, for now. Perhaps it's best if you left. When you come to your senses and stop thinking only about yourself, maybe then we can resume our conversation."

Her averted gaze, her red cheeks, and her resolute chin formed a more imposing wall than the one surrounding and protecting New Eden.

Adam nodded. He gathered the papers and empty soft drink bottles from their picnic lunch, and without another word, reluctantly stepped down from the bleachers.

He tossed the trash into a wooden barrel by the baseball backstop, then turned and headed home.

CHAPTER 15
WORDS OF THE PREACHER

ADAM waited, head lowered, sitting on a white train station bench just outside the main gates and high walls of New Eden. Just a hundred yards away, Simon Friend stared through gray iron bars into one of three holding cells in the sub-basement of the Main Administration building.

Neither the narrow hall nor the holding cells had windows. Light from two lamps cast yellow circles across bare, cold concrete.

Lucius Morris stood to Simon's right. He reached out and clanged his clipboard across the bars.

The man lying in a disheveled heap on the cell's damp floor twitched, then stirred slightly. His puffy eyes cracked open. His swollen lips, caked with dried blood, parted slightly. A wavering hand rose stiffly from his side to lightly touch his bruised and purple face.

Simon frowned and removed his long robe. With narrowed eyes, he stared out from under the mane of white hair that hung wildly about his head and purple shirt. "His name, again?"

"William O'Reilly," Lucius answered. "But he goes by the name of Joey."

Simon gripped the bars with both hands. The lamp directly behind him cast a long shadow over Joey as he worked himself slowly onto one elbow.

"And what new information have your deputies been able to get out of him?"

"Nothing more than we had last night. He refuses to explain why he was poking around the West Side and asking questions about you and Mike McDonald. What our undercover deputies didn't hear, they got directly from the people Joey talked to, mostly at the Nine-Ball Pool Hall.

Simon's eyes fell to the near motionless figure still sprawled on the cell floor.

Lucius continued. "I still don't know where he got the idea that Mike McDonald was about to pull his businesses out of the West Side. And something about a fire?"

The soft scuffle of boot leather on concrete preceded Joey's scratchy, cracked voice. "Words of the preacher, three, three. That's a riddle to you from me, McGee."

Lucius slipped his clipboard under his arm and shook his head. "Maybe a day and half without any food or water is a little too much. Now he's mumbling nonsensical rhymes."

Simon stiffened at the mention of his former name. Impossible! How could they know about his real name? Simon tightened his grip on the cell's iron bars, his eyes darting wildly between Joey and his chief of security. Fortunately, the name McGee would not mean anything to Lucius.

Then Simon suddenly realized the meaning in Joey's cryptic phrase. Lucius, obviously unfamiliar with that Bible passage, had not recognized the "words of the preacher" for what they were, a reference to the book of Ecclesiastes. And "three, three" pointed to a chapter and a verse—indeed, a most familiar passage.

A time to kill, and a time to heal; a time to break down, and a time to build up.

Simon's heart hammered hard in his chest as Joey smiled from the shadows. How could they possibly know about his plans to burn Chicago's West Side?

Simon forced himself to remain absolutely calm. They could not know. They had to be acting on an improbable hunch. Still, their hunch had struck home like an arrow in a bull's-eye.

For several moments, Simon considered silencing Joey on the spot, but reason prevailed. Simon knew he needed to find out how Vestry and his sidekick had discovered his real identity.

Turning toward Lucius, Simon willed his voice calm. "No water, no food. And for the time being, no contact. I don't want anyone talking to him, unless I'm here. Is that perfectly clear?"

Lucius shot Simon a quizzical look. "Perfectly clear."

"And keep a close eye on Christine Thompson. I don't want to find out Vestry slipped in here without anyone knowing it."

"No worries there. Kate's not letting her out of her sight. And Kate claims that Vestry left Christine on less than pleasant terms and that Christine's ready to talk to about it. Deputy Harris, my assistant, has confirmed from the duty reports that Christine and Vestry did have an argument on the bleachers this afternoon."

"Good." With a wave of his arm, Simon motioned Lucius to lead the way down the hall and out the door.

Simon spun around, ground his teeth in anger, and then slammed the solid wooden door with all his might.

The hallway shook with a resounding boom.

Monday morning had not come quickly enough for Adam. He swiftly bathed, dressed and ate.

Standing at the front desk, he had forced a smile and a "good morning" to Mrs. Phillips, then asked for his newspaper and his messages. The gray-haired boardinghouse manager handed him the morning edition of the Chicago Tribune but shook her head no about the messages.

Adam looked over at the grandfather clock to the left of the front desk. The hands pointed to seven o'clock.

Adam folded the Tribune as he turned on his heels and headed for the front door. A thin, balding man mostly hidden behind an opened newspaper glanced up from his chair as Adam sped by.

Standing on the wooden sidewalk outside, Adam slapped the newspaper against his leg. Four days and still no word from Joey! Something must have gone wrong. Terribly wrong.

He breathed in deeply and contemplated his next move as he strode down the sidewalk toward the cabby stand two blocks away. First, he would check in at the office and speak with his boss about the situation. Then he had no choice.

Joey had mentioned a half-dozen places he had planned to visit. Unfortunately, Adam remembered only two: Lefty's Bar and Grill and a pool joint called Nine Ball.

As he walked along, Adam glanced up absentmindedly at the low, gray clouds creeping in from the northwest. Deep in thought, he paid no attention to the sound of boots on the sidewalk a short distance behind him.

The thin balding man paused to fold his newspaper and adjust his bowler, then picked up his pace and followed.

Back in New Eden, Christine wrung her hands and stepped to the dormer window of her room at the Andersons'. She looked at the bank of slow-moving but widespread clouds approaching.

"Kate, what should I do? How could Adam's accusations about Simon possibly be true? But Adam's been the best of friends. He really cares for me. I treated him badly yesterday."

Kate did not answer for several moments. Christine turned around from the window. For a second, she was not sure how to read the expression on her friend's face.

Kate sat forward in the rocking chair, the trace of what might have been a smile melting downward into a frown.

"I'd like to know why Adam thinks there's a link between

organized crime and New Eden. And just because Adam says Simon is not who he says he is, doesn't mean it's so. What evidence does Adam offer to back these horrible claims?"

Christine shook her head. "He doesn't have any evidence."

Rising from her chair, Kate crossed the room and wrapped an arm around Christine.

"He doesn't have proof because there is no proof to find."

Kate looked Christine in the eye and spoke gently. "All the evidence you need is right before your eyes. Look around this room that has been freely provided. Look in your closet at the clothes you've been given. Look out the window at the wide, clean streets. Look at the schoolhouse you teach in, and the dozen others like it."

Christine looked away, biting softly at her lip.

"This is not the first time I've heard rumors like these," Kate added, releasing Christine. "People like to attack New Eden because life is so different here from life out there. They have violence. We have peace. They have crime. We have order. They have the poor. We eat until we are filled. Chicagoans seem to face troubles at every turn, while we in New Eden enjoy a little paradise every day."

Christine turned silently back to the window and stared at the barren trees lining the avenue below, then raised her hands and touched her fingertips to the cold glass.

"Yes, I suppose you're right."

CHAPTER 16
TIGHTENED SECURITY

ADAM climbed down from his cab to the wooden sidewalk, paid the driver his fare and tipped him generously.

"Thanks," Adam said with a wave. The old-timer nodded and tipped his hat, then clucked his horse back into motion.

This section of Chicago's West Side, Adam admitted to himself, was pretty seedy. Every other building or shop needed a new roof or a fresh coat of paint. The muddy rutted street needed paving badly. The old-timer struggled with his cab through the cloying brown goo that grabbed and resisted every lift of his horse's hooves and every turn of his carriage's wheels.

But it wasn't just the lack of care that created the ill feeling in Adam. From where he stood, Adam could clearly read the names of three show houses, eight bars and taverns, and five pool halls. The honky-tonk sounds of more than one upright piano could already be heard. A handful of bleary-eyed men, short, tall, and in-between, stood in open doorways with thumbs tucked in their vest pockets or belts. Short and long cigars, both brown and green, dangled from their mouths. Individual clouds of gray smoke rose about their heads and dark hats.

Adam glanced down. The long, uneven stretches of sidewalks and wooden steps that guided one to these fine establishments didn't look like they'd been washed down since the last rainstorm.

His boots squished in a dark layer of ashy grime, peppered with nasty-looking flecks of food and debris smeared with mud and who knew what else from hundreds of boots. In some places, the grime disguised sections of boards that had almost rotted through.

Apart from trying to find out what happened to Joey, Adam realized, quite literally, he would have to watch his step!

The two-foot square sign of a large black sphere with a white 9 directly in its center hung from the front door above Adam.

The Nine Ball, Adam said to himself with a smile. Had to be.

As Adam walked down an aisle between two rows of green felt-covered pool tables and several cigar-puffing customers, he did not notice the thin man with a dark bowler who stopped outside. The man leaned against the frame of the large, plate glass window and gently shook open his newspaper.

Adam took a seat at the bar amid the clack of ricocheting pool balls all around him.

"Cup of coffee, please," he said to the bartender who stood facing the opposite direction, making notations on a small pad.

The bartender glanced over his shoulder. His black hair was slicked back and shone with oil. His face, lean and weathered, sported a carefully trimmed black moustache. His dark eyebrows raised ever so slightly.

"Sure. Anything else I can get for you?" The bartender put down his pencil and walked toward the left end of the bar.

Adam reached up and rubbed the side of his face. After striking out badly at Lefty's, the Nine Ball was his last chance to find information that might lead to Joey.

"Maybe." He waited until the bartender set the steaming porcelain mug on the bar in front of him. Adam slipped a folded bill onto the bar. A bill that would pay for the coffee fifty times over.

"I'm trying to find a friend, and I need some information."

The bartender planted his hands on the bar and leaned forward, his dark eyes inquisitive. He glanced at the folded bill and nodded. "Ask away."

Adam sipped at the thick coffee, coughed lightly, then cleared his throat. The bitter coffee gave him a few extra seconds to gather his thoughts.

"He goes by the name Joey. Short, medium build, high forehead, dark hair and a heavy New York accent. I believe he was here last Thursday or Friday night. And knowing Joey, he probably sat right about here, with a similar mug of this black brew, and talked to you."

The corner of the bartender's mouth showed the beginnings of a smile. "Why, I might just remember a man who fits your story."

Adam tried to hide his relief. "OK. Now, how about the information?"

The bartender looked at the folded bill and back to Adam, his smile disappearing.

Adam reached into his vest pocket and then slid a second folded bill on top of the first.

The bartender's odd little smile returned. "Your question?"

"Joey and I are interested in a rumor. Someone's spreading the word that ol' Mike is planning to pull his businesses out of the West Side. And on very short notice."

The bartender's eyes narrowed. "A rumor, I'd say. And only a rumor."

"How can you be so sure?" Adam asked, edging forward on his stool.

The bartender lowered his head, his voice deadly serious. "'Cause I'm one of Mike's cousins. And the only cousin he likes."

Adam slowly sat back and took another sip of coffee, trying to digest the new information. So, Mike McDonald wasn't clearing out the West Side. Then maybe his theory about McGee and the timberlands and the burning of the West Side wasn't true at all?

Adam was still staring straight ahead when the bartender

scooped up the two bills and moved down the bar toward a new customer.

Adam found himself looking into a mirror behind the bar, seeing his own reflection, mug clutched between his hands. Behind him he saw rows of pool tables and drifting clouds of smoke. And beyond the smoke, Adam suddenly noticed a thin man with a dark bowler, standing outside, staring through the wide window at him.

Abruptly, the man turned his back to the window, snapping his newspaper open in what was meant to be a casual motion.

A cold chill fell over Adam. Twice before, when he was in New York, Adam had been tailed. And now, just like then, Adam experienced that same creepy feeling of discovering that someone was following him.

Adam rose from his stool and turned to face the front window.

It came as no surprise that the man with the newspaper had already disappeared.

Adam started to leave, then turned around and waited until he had caught the bartender's eye.

"One last question?" Adam asked.

The bartender nodded.

"Did my friend talk to anyone else while he was here?"

A familiar smile crept back onto the bartender's face. "So you're not as dumb as I thought. Yeah, sure. He talked with a couple guys. In fact, he left with one of them."

Alarm struck Adam's face. And he knew the bartender had seen his surprise.

"Do you know the man Joey left with that night?"

The bartender grabbed a cloth and started wiping the top of the bar. "Seen him in here a couple times before, I'm sure. If I remember right, I don't think he's local. Not to Chicago, anyway."

The bartender kept wiping, his eyes lowered.

"And?" Adam asked as he reached into his vest pocket.

The circular motion of his cloth came to a sudden stop.

"And that's all I'm going to tell you. Keep your money. Now if you're as smart as I think you are, you'll stop asking questions and get a move on."

Adam complied.

Back in New Eden, Simon Friend watched Christine Thompson's roommate through the one-way mirror as she spoke with Lucius in the People's Deputies meeting room.

Kate repeatedly clasped and unclasped her hands, her face lined with concern. Lucius nodded, made a final note on his clipboard, and dismissed her.

Simon did not like the sour look on Lucius' face as he turned and approached the door to his office.

"This is not good news," the chief of security said as walked into the room. He quickly detailed Kate's account of her conversation with Christine and of how Vestry was investigating a link between New Eden and organized crime.

"And Vestry also believes that you're someone different than you claim to be. That you have connections back to a place called Paradise."

Simon noticed that Lucius was carefully watching his face. He kept his emotions in check, as he finally understood how Vestry and his sidekick had come up with his real name. Somehow they had traced him back to that blasted little Pennsylvania town where he had made his first million some thirty years ago.

But that was part of his past he didn't want Lucius, or anyone else, to learn about.

Simon casually tapped his chin. "Vestry's working on hearsay. He doesn't have any proof to support his allegations. And with his sidekick and Christine safely behind our walls, we can cut off his key sources of information."

Lucius looked as if he wanted to speak, but instead made a note on his clipboard.

"As of this moment, Vestry's banned from entering New Eden," Simon continued, turning to face the one-way mirror. "And put the deputies on alert about Christine. I don't want her leaving the grounds."

"Should we screen her mail, too?"

Simon nodded gravely. "Yes, incoming and outgoing. No leaks."

"And what about Mr. McDonald?" Lucius asked. "Shouldn't we notify him about all of this?"

"Absolutely not," Simon replied, spinning around suddenly. "We don't need to bother him with your internal security problems. And I don't think that you want him sending over his goons to question you about these problems, do you?"

Lucius' hand and pencil froze over the clipboard.

"I didn't think you did," Simon replied, answering his own question.

He smiled grimly and left the room.

Her classes over for the day, Christine followed the required security procedure and locked the door to her schoolroom. She turned around to find Kate standing at the street.

Christine waved as she came down the sidewalk. "Hi. How was your day?"

"Pretty busy, I guess," Kate replied with a shrug, lowering her chin into the collar of her long wool coat and glancing away.

"Yeah. Mine, too." Christine paused. "Why the sad look? Is something wrong?"

Kate lifted her gaze to Christine. "No. Everything's fine."

Kate offered a weak smile and then linked arms with Christine.

"Come on. Let's go home, get ready for dinner, and think of something pleasant to do this evening."

CHAPTER 17
CLOUDED REFLECTIONS

UNDER the thick cloud cover blanketing the city, the famous Chicago winds came sweeping in. Adam turned up his collar and walked more briskly down the wooden sidewalk toward his boardinghouse.

The wind clawed at his hair and ran cold fingers up the sleeves of his coat. He lowered his head and pressed on. In moments, he was through the painted glass doors and inside into the warmth.

Immediately, he lifted his eyes and gazed around the room. To the right, he recognized the young couple sitting on the tweed sofa near the fireplace. One read an evening newspaper; the other flipped through a fresh-off-the-press copy of *The Nation*.

To the left, four leather high-backed chairs surrounded a circular tea table. Two of the chairs were taken. Adam did not recognize either guest. In one, an elderly man leaned comfortably with his head tilted back, eyes closed, hands lightly gripping the armrests. In the other chair, a pert young woman with auburn hair made notes in a small blue journal, putting words to paper with precise, smooth motions.

Adam continued toward the stairs, his senses on alert, wondering if he had seen her somewhere before. Now that he knew he was being followed, every new face and every heard but unseen footfall jolted him with unease. He climbed the three flights to his room, hearing only the creak of his own boots on the wooden steps.

Once in his room, Adam locked the door and lit a lamp. In a growing circle of yellow light, he slipped off his jacket, tossed it on the end of his bed, and went to the window. As he removed his cufflinks and rolled up his sleeves, he looked down at the now familiar view of Chicago's North Side.

So much had happened in only two weeks!

His heart ached. Christine had moved to New Eden and been seduced by Simon Friend and his phony workers' paradise. Joey, his new friend, had disappeared under dangerous and suspicious circumstances.

And in a way, Adam knew that his past had come back to haunt him. Not only in the person of Lucius Morris, but in another deadly game of cat-and-mouse where he had become the mouse yet again!

Adam sat on his bed and lay back. He put his hands behind his head and stared at the ceiling, his thoughts circling around and around as he pondered his next move.

Simon Friend was hunched over his desk in the Grand Room. A strong gust of wind rattled the tall windows at the opposite end of the room, making him peer up from the city map spread out in front of him.

The fireplace roared too, as the winds swirled over the wooden shingles and over the chimney on the Main Administration building's roof. The rising flames cast a bright red glow over Simon's face, the city map, and the panorama of futuristic Chicago covering the length of the opposite wall.

Simon grinned.

When they rebuilt Chicago's West Side the next time, the value of the real estate would skyrocket. New buildings, new railroads, new mansions for the wealthy.

Simon hungrily turned back to the map and circled ten

strategically located city blocks. With the money from the illegal kickbacks he had been saving for the past five years, as well as some of the profits he had skimmed from Mike McDonald's share, he could afford to buy over twenty-seven prime acres—a little over a square mile—right in the middle of the West Side.

Simon ran the tip of his index finger along the city streets surrounding the blocks of buildings that would soon be his. He would buy the buildings one by one, then block by block.

Yes, buying up the real estate would take every last dollar he had saved—except his private stash of cash and gems hidden in the wall safe behind the portrait of King Nebuchadnezzar.

He paused to catch his breath, his chest swelling with pride. Vestry and his sidekick would not stop him now. Weak-willed Lucius would no longer be allowed to delay him. The clock was ticking, and he would soon silence them all, forever.

Simon sat straight up and threw his head back. His long white hair, filled with static and fanned about his head and shoulders, gleamed orange and red like the crackling fire. He thrust his arms high above his head, lifted his chin and shouted, his voice bold and trembling at the same time.

"Destiny awaits me!"

Christine shivered as cold wind slipped through the cracks of her window and brushed across her arms.

She pulled her shawl around her shoulders. Tonight, there were no stars, no moon. The thick cloud cover had seen to that. New Eden was dark and cold, even though the intermittent circles of gaslights bordering the avenue lit the way of the two deputies strolling below.

Every minute or so, Christine could hear Kate behind her, shifting in her rocker by the fireplace or turning the pages of her book. She liked Kate, she really did.

But lately, Kate had seemed to hover close around, always

within speaking distance. Going to their schoolrooms, coming from the schoolrooms, going to the dining hall and returning. At a workshop and a play and even on quiet walks, Kate was always there. Smiling. Friendly. Helpful. But always there.

Christine lowered her eyes. Filled but not satisfied by what she had eaten at dinner, she remembered the wonderful meal Adam had treated her to on the train from Paradise to Chicago. And though she did not want to admit it, she did miss her Aunt Agnes.

Now, twenty long miles of railroad track separated her from the two people she wanted to spend time with the most. And though the high walls and connecting towers that she could see from almost any place in New Eden still made her feel secure, they also made her feel hemmed in, contained, like a bird in a cage. A big cage, for sure, but still a cage.

Hearing herself sigh, Christine brought her hand to her mouth and hoped Kate had not noticed. Despite her private misgivings, she did not want to trouble her friend.

Kate was a hard worker, too, always trying her best. And now that Kate knew about her feelings and about her arguments with Adam, Kate had begun to carry Christine's burden, as well.

At first, everything had seemed so straightforward, so right. Then Adam had come along and ruined everything! Making her own way was hard enough. Why was he trying to make it harder?

Clutching the corners of the shawl, Christine crossed her hands beneath her chin, her eyes following a broad oak leaf that twirled in the wind just outside her window.

The light from the fire and the lamp reflected off the shiny surface of the leaf as it dipped and rose and dipped again. Then, in blink of her eye, the wind gusted and the leaf was gone, swept upward and away into the darkness.

CHAPTER 18

SNUFF THE LAMPS

CHICAGO woke to a gray morning sky and a chilling breeze. In the dining room of Phillip's Boardinghouse, Adam picked at several silver-dollar pancakes and sipped his cup of coffee. His appetite had been dulled by the idea that struck him as he splashed his face with water after climbing out of bed. He left his morning paper unread beside his plate, grabbed a hard-boiled egg from a wooden bowl in the center of the table and smiled at a curious Mrs. Phillips on his way out.

He stopped at the front desk, not expecting to find a message from Joey, but he checked anyway. He thanked the sleepy-eyed clerk and turned for the door.

The fireplace-warmed foyer had only one guest this morning—the same auburn-haired young woman Adam had seen the night before. She held an open copy of *The Nation* and appeared deep in thought.

Adam pushed open the front door and turned right. He crossed the street at the corner, avoided several deep ruts in the street, and stepped up onto the wooden sidewalk on the opposite side. He headed to the right and in minutes found himself standing directly in front of Christine's aunt's mansion.

He took a deep breath, started up the walk to the house and

silently prayed that his idea would prove correct. He reached up and pulled on the doorbell.

Less than a minute later, the oval face of Spinster Thompson's maid appeared in the narrow, rectangular window to the right of the door.

The door swung open. The maid's black dress and white apron were flawlessly neat. She smiled.

"Good morning, Mr. Vestry. What may I do for you?"

Adam returned the smile. "I was hoping to speak with Christine's aunt."

"Oh, I'm so sorry," the maid said slowly. "Miss Thompson is away for the week. She's in Boston attending a healing conference being held by Mrs. Mary Baker Glover."

Adam's countenance fell sharply. "I guess I've struck out twice then. First wanting to see Christine, now her aunt."

"Would you like to leave a message for when she returns?"

"I could, but the timing would be all wrong. You see, I was hoping that Christine's aunt might allow me to look at the book Christine brought back with her from Paradise. It's quite tall, but thin. A clothbound journal."

The maid stood silently for a moment, then her smiled returned. "Please come in."

Adam nodded and entered the foyer. The maid closed the door behind him and then headed away, down a long hall to the right. He looked around and let go with a long, but nearly inaudible whistle at the marble floor and staircase, the crystal chandelier and the heavy drapes.

The clack of the maid's shoes preceded her presence coming down the hall. As she approached, Adam saw that she had brought the book with her.

Suddenly hopeful, Adam reined in his excitement and folded his hands politely in front of him.

"Here you are," the maid offered, holding out the book to

Adam.

He took it and clutched it with both hands. "Where would you like me to sit and read it?"

The maid looked momentarily confused, then righted herself as Adam quickly opened the journal and flipped through the first dozen pages, his eyes consuming the neat, handwritten script.

"Oh, no. Please take it. When Miss Agnes sent the book, she never expected it back."

Adam paused at one page in particular, grinned broadly and then bowed, closing the book in one smooth motion.

"I can't thank you enough. And neither can Christine, believe me. She just doesn't know it yet!"

Two stories beneath the Main Administration building, New Eden's chief of security swung open the door to the sub-basement holding cells.

Simon Friend, dressed in his usual white pants and purple shirt, stood with his hands behind his back and waited outside the doorway. With a nod of his head, he signaled the two deputies he had asked Lucius to bring along. They entered the shadowed hall, lit two oil lamps, and then quietly left the room.

"Wait outside," Simon said directly to the deputies as he stepped past Lucius and walked straight to the middle cell.

He turned and watched as Lucius carried a brass pail half filled with water and set it near the corner of the iron bars.

"Wake him." Simon commanded loudly.

Lucius grabbed the pail and started to swing it, but a husky, voice rattled out from the cell.

"No, don't—I'm awake."

Simon eyed Lucius and tipped his head toward the iron bars. Lucius flung the water into the center of the cell.

Joey gasped as the water spilled over his head and around his shoulders. But he struggled up on his elbows, cupping his hands in time to capture a few ounces of water that splashed into his open palms. He carefully and slowly lapped at the water.

Simon stepped back, allowing the lamp light to fall over Adam Vestry's water-soaked sidekick, huddled and shaking on the drenched concrete floor. His eyes and mouth were no longer swollen, but his face was still heavily purpled from bruises.

Joey lifted his head and stared at Simon through squinted eyes. His hair was matted flat in twisted clumps. Water dripped from the end of his nose and stubbly chin.

"Figure out my riddle, McGee?" he asked defiantly in a scratchy voice.

Simon grinned and shook his head. He ignored the quick turn of Lucius' head and his surprised expression.

"You and Vestry are fools. Do you truly think that you can stop me? In fact, Vestry doesn't even know you're here. Your life is totally in my hands."

Joey pushed himself to his knees and cleared phlegm from his throat. "Maybe so. But you're an even bigger fool if you think ol' Mike's gonna just sit back and smoke one of his big stogies while you're out setting fire to Chicago's West Side."

Lucius reached out and grabbed the sleeve of Simon's shirt, his face twisting with pain. Bitterness etched his words. "How could you even consider it after what happened at Peshtigo? Two thousand people died!"

Joey looked from Lucius to Simon. Horror dawned in his eyes.

Lucius grimaced and shook his head. "Now I know why you didn't want me to contact Mike McDonald. You've been planning this for quite some time, haven't you?"

Silence stole into the room as Lucius' eyes darkened. "And the name, McGee—that is your name, isn't it?"

Simon ripped his arm away, lifted his chin and looked down his nose at his chief of security—his "former" chief of security. Then

Simon signaled with his right hand.

His two handpicked deputies came quickly down the hall.

"Harris, open the first cell, please."

The taller of the two deputies took a key chain from his back pocket and unlocked the cell. The other deputy patted his hands over Lucius' shirt and pants, found Lucius' set of keys and yanked them from his pocket; then, he threw an elbow in the middle of Lucius' back and shoved him stumbling into the cell.

Lucius slowly turned around, drew himself to full height and watched in dismay as Harris, his one-time assistant, slammed the cell door. The iron bars banged loudly and locked into place with a sharp click.

Simon smoothed the wrinkles from his shirtsleeve. "I've seen this coming now, for weeks. Your conscience continues to fail you, Lucius. Harris, here, doesn't have your weak stomach. Just look at Joey. I know you agree that Harris does the dirty work with enthusiasm."

Joey edged forward on his knees and wrapped his grimy hands around the iron bars.

"You're a lunatic, McGee. A certifiable lunatic."

Without warning, Simon lashed out his leg and smashed his boot over the cell's bars and Joey's fingers.

Joey cried out and fell back, his bleeding hands curled in pain.

"How dare you call me a lunatic!" Simon roared, grabbing the empty pail and slamming it against the cell bars over and over again. Joey, Lucius and the two deputies flinched with every ear-splitting ring of brass on iron. After expending his rage, he tossed the heavily dented pail into the corner with yet another noisy clang.

Then he turned and brought his bulging eyes and contorted mouth up close to the bars.

"You're lucky to be alive," Simon growled, breathing hard and staring through knotted strands of white hair that hung down across his face.

Simon stepped to Lucius' cell and spat on his former chief of security's boots.

"Both of you."

Simon looked to his right and pointed a finger at Harris' face.

"Snuff the lamps. No water. No food. If by chance I forget about these two, come back in a week and bury the bodies in the refuse pile. They'll make great compost. And if none of your deputies can handle the job properly, then do it yourself!"

CHAPTER 19
MARY ELIZABETH MCGEE

IGNORING the bustle of passengers around him, Adam stared up at the imposing white walls and wrought iron gates of New Eden. He clutched an old brown leather satchel in one hand and nervously fingered a small tan card—the visitor pass Simon had given him the week before—with his other hand.

Adam drew a deep breath and headed for the gates.

Right away, something seemed different, wrong. And in moments, he had figured out what it was.

Today, the tall main gates were closed. All foot traffic was routed through a smaller set of gates built right into the center where the main gates came together. The open archway in the thick iron bars was wide enough for only two people to pass through at a time, creating a logjam on either side of the opening.

Adam could do nothing but wait his turn. He gripped the satchel's handle a little tighter as he stepped beneath the arch.

"Hold on, right there."

Two gray-shirted deputies blocked Adam's way. Both were a head taller than Adam, and wider.

"Your pass, please?"

Adam handed him the tan card. "Any problems?"

"Problem. Yeah, there's a problem all right," the deep-voiced deputy said as he stuffed the pass into his shirt pocket. "You're going to leave the premises immediately and get on that waiting train."

"I have an appointment with Simon Friend. There must be some mistake." From the souring expressions on the deputies' faces, Adam could guess what the answer would be.

"You're the mistake. Now get out of here. Under your own power or with a little help. You pick." The deputy smiled, lifted his arm and made a tight fist.

Adam swallowed hard. The deputy's biceps were as big as most men's necks!

He turned around and headed back toward the station.

Standing on the platform beside the station house, Adam's hopes plummeted like the iron bolt he'd tossed into the Chicago River that night with Joey.

He was so close! Christine was less than a half mile away, in her schoolroom and unaware that the proof she had wanted now stood inside the satchel resting by his feet, bound with string and wrapped in plain brown paper.

But what could he do? The deputies had been on the lookout, waiting for him to show up. And whatever was going on inside those high white walls could only mean trouble. Joey could even be there, if, Adam thought dejectedly, he wasn't wearing a new pair of cement shoes on the bottom of the Chicago River.

Adam crossed his arms and drummed the fingers of one hand on his chin. He wracked his brain, trying to envision how he might possibly get the paper-wrapped package into Christine's hands.

His fingers stopped drumming. Wait! If he, himself, couldn't get the journal to her—

Maybe someone else could!

While two elderly women in bright flowered dresses squabbled with the frazzled ticket clerk, Adam slid back up to the counter and nonchalantly returned the leaking pen to the inkwell.

"Excuse me," he said with a smile, parting the now indignant women to either side with his satchel. He worked his way to a window and then checked his hands, front and back, for any signs of ink.

So far, so good.

He watched as the three men wearing white shirts carefully arranged various parcels and letters in three shallow wooden crates. Then, crates in hand, they headed up the cobblestone walkway toward New Eden.

Adam paused for a second and grinned.

The first part of his plan just might work.

The shriek of the train whistle cut through the air. Adam hurried through the stationhouse and worked his way to the nearest train car. He bounded up the metal steps past the startled conductor, then spun around on the narrow platform between the two cars.

The three men in white shirts had disappeared into New Eden.

The whistle sounded a second time, and the train jerked slightly and started chugging down the tracks to Chicago.

Adam took several deep breaths.

Now came the dangerous part!

"Students, you did a very good job on that vocabulary lesson," Christine said cheerfully. "But now it's time for math."

The schoolroom echoed with a smattering of groans.

Christine began to open the math book in front of her, but was interrupted by a knock on the door. But before she could turn from the desk, the door opened part way.

"Mail call, Ma'am." The man said, poking his head and arm inside the door.

Christine, unsure of what to do, did not reach for the package.

"Who is this for?"

The man looked at the name inked on the front. "Says 'Blue Sector. School Number Two. Elementary 3 and 4.' That's this school room, right? Do you want it, or should I return it to the postal boys and let them open it."

Christine knew she had not ordered any books. She raised her hand and was about to refuse the package, but then changed her mind.

"Just leave it by the door. Thanks."

Turning back to her desk, Christine opened the math book and smiled.

"Turn to page thirty, please."

The groans returned.

Lunchtime approached, but Adam ignored the growl in his stomach. He handed the cabby his fare and leapt from the carriage to the wooden sidewalk. He glanced up at the large painted sign of a black nine ball and hurried inside.

Adam brushed away a cloud of thick cigar smoke that wafted in his face, then headed straight for the bar. He hardly heard the deep-voiced chatter of the Nine Ball's patrons or the crack of scattering pool balls. The bartender, wiping glass mugs behind the bar, watched Adam approach. The hint of a smile lifted the corner of his carefully trimmed moustache.

Adam steeled himself as he slapped both hands down onto the top of the bar and told the bartender what he wanted.

Caught completely off guard by Adam's request, all the bartender could do was laugh.

Another school day in New Eden was over. Christine sat down at the small oak table in her room as Kate hung their coats in the wardrobe by the door.

She squeezed the scissors and cut the string around the package. Something about the size and shape of the book seemed very familiar. Then, as she pulled back the wrapping, she saw the clothbound corner and knew.

The journal! The shock had hardly even begun to subside when she found the small note sticking up from between the pages. She pulled it out. Adam!

She read the note. The gentle, kind words stung her more than any spanking her father or mother had ever given her.

Kate stopped beside the table and saw the journal, the note in Christine's hands and the expression on her face. She slowly pulled out a chair and sat down beside her.

Eyes tearing, Christine looked up and handed Kate the note. She watched Kate's eyes follow Adam's bold, clean cursive down the small sheet of notepaper.

Then Christine opened the journal and read the neat handwritten words at the top of the page: *Paradise Lost,* by Mary Elizabeth McGee.

Adam followed the bartender, Jack McDonald, out the back of the Nine Ball. As they hurried down the uneven wooden planks of a narrow Chicago West Side alley, the winds picked up. Loose pieces of trash swirled about their feet. Shortly, they came to a T. The bartender turned right down another alley, then knocked four times on the first door to his left: two quick knocks followed by a pause, then two more quick knocks.

The door swung open. The bartender quickly slipped inside the dark hall. Adam stepped forward over the threshold, then hesitated.

A tall, broad-shouldered man with a pockmarked face and a dark scowl stood just inside the doorway.

"Well, what are you waiting for," he asked in a soft but gravelly, baritone voice, "an invitation or something?"

New Eden had never seemed so cold.

Kate stoked the fire as Christine continued to read aloud Mary Elizabeth McGee's story about her husband Simon's cruel scheme to defraud the people and town of Paradise.

Christine's voice rose and fell with Mary Elizabeth's emotional recounting of the summer and fall of 1846 when Simon brought the small Pennsylvania town to the brink of ruin.

The lure of harmony and peace captured the hearts of men and women alike. The continued political battles over slavery and the growing divide between the North and the South only made Simon's claims more attractive.

But his promise of a shared prosperity enthralled the townspeople even more. The people of Junction Creek, as the town was called before Simon convinced them to change the name to Paradise, were produce and dairy farmers. Just the year before, two back-to-back floods had devastated the town. The floods had also torn away part of a hillside, exposing a series of natural caves.

How Simon had come to own that hill and the long ridge it was a part of, I will never know. But when Simon declared that gold had been discovered in his caves, I suspected that once again Simon had used people's tragic circumstances for his own gain, as he had done in New York five years earlier. And it does not matter that he brought in engineers to support his claims, or that several townspeople found shining gold nuggets in the hills and panned a small amount of gold dust from the creeks.

Simon was clever. He knew engineers could be bought and the cost of his imported gold could be recovered one hundred times over. Within two months, he parceled and sold the rights to dozens of mines, as well as supplying the equipment and services of an excavating company to dig and frame out the mines—all at a handsome profit.

My husband disappeared that fall, with all of the money, before the townspeople would finally discover that not another nugget or grain of gold dust would ever be found. Afterwards, they pitied me, all too kindly I will add. For it was the founding families of Junction Creek, now a Paradise Lost, who suffered so greatly.

And their dreams of a heaven on earth, where men, women and children can work side by side toward a common purpose and for a higher good, fell into ruin. Their faith shaken, some turned their backs on God, holding Him in judgment for their misadventures.

But some, realizing the foolishness of their ways, turned back to God, putting their hands to the plow and rebuilding their lives, once again. For these, the bitter lesson Simon McGee taught them will never be forgotten.

Nor shall I ever forget him, a good man in his youth. Even as the sudden turn of his once-brown hair to a pure, lifeless white, truth gave way to lies. Simon traded his soul for the rewards of Mammon and never once looked back.

Christine closed the journal and looked up, tears streaming down her cheeks. Kate was crestfallen too, her face ashen.

"Everything Adam was trying to tell me was true." Christine wiped her eyes with her fingertips. "New Eden is a lie. Simon is a liar. He's using us, just like he used the people of Paradise.

"I wanted so much to believe that there was nothing wrong here that I ignored all the signs." Christine stared at the journal. "And Sunday, when Simon went on and on, twisting the Scriptures, I just pushed my concerns aside. I deceived myself into believing that his gemstone breastplate and his nonsensical preaching really didn't matter. All that mattered was my teacher position."

Kate nodded silently, wiping her own misty eyes.

"But now I know that's not true. I can't stay, Kate. I just can't."

Suddenly, Kate raised her hands to her face, started to weep, and then seemed to force herself to look up. Her mouth trembled.

"Oh, Christine! I've done such a terrible thing! How will you ever forgive me?"

Christine sniffled, then scooted her chair closer to Kate. "What do you mean? You're one of my dearest friends."

The words seemed to cut deeply into Kate, but she reached out and clutched Christine's hands, fighting back sobs.

"I've been spying on you. Reporting to Lucius, our chief of security, about your relationship with Adam. I'm what we call a plainclothes deputy. I just don't wear gray and black."

Kate's eyes met Christine's at last. "At first, Lucius told me that you were working with Adam to falsely incriminate Simon and New Eden. Some of the daily tabloids are nothing but muckrakers anyway, so I believed him. But as I got to know you, I knew in my heart you were just who you said you were—my friend!"

Christine squeezed Kate's hands and offered her the warmest smile she could muster. "It's all right. We've both been duped. But now we know the truth. And we don't have to stay. I'm sure my aunt will allow you to stay with us until we figure out what to do."

Kate's face brightened a little. She nodded.

Christine stood up. "I say we pack the few things we actually own and slip out of here—now."

She glanced at the clock on the mantel. "And if we hurry, we can catch the evening train to Chicago."

CHAPTER 20
'OL MIKE

DEEP in the center of Chicago's West Side, in a run-down and deserted warehouse, Adam Vestry sat upright in a hard wooden chair and wanted to pinch himself. At this journalistic opportunity of a lifetime, Adam wanted to make sure he was actually awake and not dreaming.

Adam looked across a highly polished but completely bare cherry desk and studied the deadpan expression on the face of Michael McDonald, Chicago's most famous crime boss, or, more properly stated, Chicago's most famous 'alleged' crime boss.

Michael McDonald's eyes were dark, thoughtful pools. More like quicksand than water, Adam mused. He couldn't tell if ol' Mike, as Joey so often called him, was angry, interested or even pleased with what he had just learned about Simon Friend, a.k.a. Simon McGee.

Ol' Mike looked slowly over to the right. Eyeing his scar-faced handyman for a second, he turned to face his cousin. The moustached bartender met his gaze as he ran a comb through his oiled hair.

"Well, Jack, what do you think?" Mike asked.

Jack slipped his comb back into his jacket pocket. "I believe him. Joey left the Nine Ball that night with one of New Eden's deputies. At the time, I couldn't connect all the facts. But now, I believe Adam could be right about this. It all adds up. It's just hard to believe that Friend could so stupid! Burn down the West Side? He's a fool!"

The pockmark-faced man spoke up. "Much as it pains me to say, Mike, we've been suckered. And after helping Friend with all those sweet deals—"

Ol' Mike frowned and waggled his index finger. His handyman abruptly clamped his mouth shut. Mike tugged at the lapels of his dark blue, pinstriped suit. He leaned over his desk and brought his hands together, slowly closing his fingers into a steeple.

"I've always said Friend and his deputies were nothing but a bunch of two-bit hoodlums. So Friend thinks he can torch my town? I don't think so."

Then Ol' Mike peered up at his handyman. "Horace, I want you and Jack to get the boys together right away. Friend's not just a fool, but an unpredictable fool. He should've learned by now that you shouldn't plan something against others that you wouldn't want them to do back to you. And be thorough about it."

Then Mike swiveled his head and stared straight at Adam.

Adam clamped his fingers on the edge of his seat. His throat was suddenly as dry as a bone as he pictured kneeling beside Joey in the Underworld, watching his friend poke a skull with a stick.

Ol' Mike laughed.

"Now don't be worried, young man. Nothing's been said here today that'll cost you or me anything. No doubt, someday you'll want to write an article about me for that magazine of yours. Be my guest. But for now, if you have friends there in New Eden, I'd recommend that you'd best be on your way there ahead of my boys. Things could end up a little rowdy."

Ol' Mike flashed Adam a toothy smile.

"The interview is over."

As they walked around the circular fountain and headed down the cobblestone path toward New Eden's main gates, Christine glanced at

Kate with concern.

The large outer gates had been closed. Visitors and community members alike walked single file through the small interior gates under the watchful eyes of two male deputies.

"I don't know," Kate said worriedly, clutching an old haversack tightly in one hand. "Something isn't right."

"Maybe we should try another gate?" Christine asked, stopping to push the journal deeper into her book bag with the few belongings she dared try to carry out.

Kate nodded. "I agree. Let's go to the north gate. It's mostly used for—"

Simultaneously, two large hands clasped Christine and Kate on the shoulders.

Startled and off balance, the two girls suddenly found themselves spun around. Kate dropped her haversack. Christine bobbled her book bag, then grabbed it around the middle, pushing the journal up and out.

"Going somewhere, ladies?" Deputy Harris asked as he reached down and picked up the journal that had landed on the toe of his boot.

His surly voice frightened Christine. She wanted to reach out and grab the journal from his hands, but knew she would only be rebuffed.

"Hmmm. What's this?" the deputy asked, opening the journal and flipping through the pages. Then, as Christine feared, the deputy's hand stopped, his eyes reading down a page.

He lifted his head, his eyes boring into Christine's, the intensity of his stare forcing her to look away.

"Well, well. I think that Mr. Friend would be interested in this book, don't you?"

He snapped the book shut and grabbed their bags in his big fist. His loud, deep voice made the girls flinch.

"Follow me!"

* * *

Standing in the ground level foyer of the Main Administration building, Simon sighed and read the first page of the open and familiar journal.

"Mary Elizabeth McGee, my silly, weak-willed wife. How much trouble you have caused me. And now still do."

Simon shook his head, closed the book and stuck it under one arm. He signaled to Harris.

Harris turned and spoke to the red-haired, female deputy on guard behind the desk. "Please relieve the deputy on duty downstairs at the holding cells."

The woman nodded, placed her clipboard on the desk, and then walked past Harris and down to the end of the hall. She turned left and disappeared down the stairwell on the left.

Simon stared at Kate, disgust clouding his face.

"You, a People's Deputy, abandoning your loyalties and joining forces with Christine Thompson and Adam Vestry. I find your decision repugnant and worthy of punishment, like that of our former chief of security, Mr. Morris. Deputy Harris, assign her to a holding cell."

"Then what? Do you want me to ready the team?" Harris asked, grabbing Kate so tightly by the arm that she cried out.

"Yes. And make sure that wagon of fertilizers, sulfur and kerosene is carefully disguised. We don't want any back road travelers to remember anything unusual about our mobile firebomb, come tomorrow. And I want that wagon rolling within the hour. You have the location and you know what to do."

Harris nodded gravely, then turned and pulled Kate after him.

"And you, young lady, come with me!" Simon exclaimed to Christine with fire in his eyes. "I want to show you something truly grand!"

CHAPTER 21
A FLAMING PYRE

ADAM stared out the train window and wondered if he would beat Mike McDonald's hard-riding men to New Eden. They would be dashing down back roads in the bright moonlight, driving their steeds hard through wooded and rough terrain that the railroad tracks curved west to avoid.

A cold chill crept over Adam. Even though he had caught a train almost straightaway, what if Mike's men had already reached New Eden? What if they had already—

The train swept around a bend, blew its whistle and began to slow down. Adam leaned forward, his eyes searching through the stands of trees separating the tracks from a wide dirt road.

High white walls came gleaming into view. Faint streams of pale smoke drifted moonward from tall chimneys in the manufacturing and warehouse sectors directly ahead in New Eden's northernmost corner. Adam rose from his seat and moved toward the train car door. The silver-haired conductor smiled as Adam waited impatiently behind him, peering out the small window in the door as the train pulled into the station.

No signs of trouble.

Scarcely had the conductor creaked open the doors when Adam bounded past, down and off the steps toward the dull, black iron gates blanketed with shadows.

Shrugging off the icy air that stung his face, Adam strode swiftly toward the main gates. The tower to the right blocked the moonlight and hid the central section of the gates, right where Adam knew the deputies would be waiting and watching.

As Adam approached the area of deepest darkness, he prayed silently but fervently. Once before, four years ago, he had dashed off to rescue his friends from terrible danger, only to be caught, disarmed and rendered utterly useless. Though his physical wounds had been superficial, the memories of that horrible, deadly night still haunted him.

But he knew he had no choice. Didn't the Bible say, "Greater love hath no man than this, that a man lay down his life for his friends"? He would face his fear head on. God would have to do the rest.

Adam took a deep breath and entered the darkness. And what God had to do, began right now, if he had any hopes of finding and saving Christine and Joey. Adam refused to believe that his friend was dead.

A lamp fluttered to life, driving back the shadows. The yellow light revealed two broad-shouldered men in dark coats and black pants. Men, Adam knew, he could not overcome by physical prowess.

"Who goes there?" a deep voice barked.

"Adam Vestry. You know who I am. Let's cut to the chase, as they say. I'm here to see Simon. I've just spent an entertaining half-hour with a Mr. Michael McDonald. Maybe you've heard of him. I have a personal message to deliver."

Adam pulled a folded square of white paper from his vest pocket and held it up between two fingers.

One of the deputies reached out for it, but Adam tucked his fingers and clutched the paper in his fist.

"You got any ears? I said a personal message. Now, open the gates. You don't want to be the deputy who got Simon in trouble with Ol' Mike, would you?"

***

On the upper floor of the Main Administration building a hundred yards away, Simon pivoted both Christine and her chair to face the panorama of futuristic Chicago. The painting glowed eerily in the flickering oranges and yellows from the fireplace.

Christine cried out as her weight shifted sideways and the ropes binding her to the chair scraped along her wrist and ankles. Then the chair's other legs came down hard to the wooden floor with a loud thump.

"Now, now, no complaining," Simon said as he leaned over and brought a handkerchief toward the corners of her eyes. His contorted face shone with reflected firelight. "I need someone to keep me company this glorious night!"

Repulsed, Christine turned her head sharply away, her strawberry-blonde hair fanning over her face.

His expression unchanging, Simon turned away.

Through a thin veil of her hair, Christine watched Simon stalk across the room to the fireplace and toss the handkerchief on the burning, ember-covered logs and now-blackened journal. The corners of the white cloth curled and then burst into flame.

Simon held out his hands to warm them, lifting his chin and shaking his mane of white hair off his shoulders. His back was to Christine, his dark silhouette lined in crimson, his thick hair a fiery cloud. His voice echoed slightly in the large room.

"The time has come, my will be done. When Harris and his deputies reach the West Side with our little Trojan Horse loaded with explosive compounds, a brand new day in the history of Chicago will dawn with its own glorious, morning light."

Christine clamped her eyes and mouth shut and worked her wrists back and forth. She had to get free! Had to somehow escape! Ignoring the pain, she could feel the ropes begin to loosen.

The brush of coarse hair against her face startled her.

She found herself staring into two, bulging white orbs with coal black centers and eyebrows arching into a V.

"Not so fast, young lady!"

Simon grabbed the loose ends of the rope and yanked hard.

Tears sprung from her eyes as Christine choked back a scream.

Adam approached the circular steps of the Main Administration building and knew the folded square of blank paper in his vest pocket would soon prove useless. Once he stood before Simon face to face, his ruse would be instantly exposed. Sure, Mike McDonald was sending Simon Friend a message, but Adam was not the one delivering it!

The deputy passed by him, climbed the steps two at a time and hurried to the double doors. They were locked. The deputy stepped back and glanced up. The long row of windows on the left end of the upper floor flickered dully with light.

"He's there, but the doors are locked. Very odd."

Adam silently expelled a deep breath and his patience. "Then unlock them. I guess I'll just have to tell Mr. McDonald how you wasted his time with stupid excuses."

The deputy frowned and pulled a jingling ring of keys from his coat pocket. For several seconds, he fumbled trying to find the correct one.

"Got it!" he said, inserting the key and turning the bolt. The deputy swung the door inward and then turned to face Adam.

For a split second, the deputy's face flashed yellow, then red.

Adam did not have time to understand the sudden burst of colors before a deafening boom rocked the night. As Adam spun to face the sound, the steps beneath his feet shook, making him struggle to maintain his balance.

Off to the right, beyond the row of trees separating the Main Administration building grounds and the manufacturing sector, a spreading mushroom of flame and black smoke rose among the warehouses and kiln. But even as the first curse broke from the deputy's mouth, his gasping voice was drowned out by three successive explosions as large as the first.

Knocked to his knees, Adam watched in stunned fascination as four flaming railroad cars rose into the air and tumbled end over end, falling away in different directions onto the roofs of surrounding warehouses.

Was this the handiwork of Ol' Mike's men?

Adam wasn't sure. He didn't know if five seconds or five minutes had passed when he finally pushed himself to his feet.

He grabbed the deputy by the arm and spun him around.

"Where does Simon keep his prisoners?" Adam yelled. The deputy tried to pull his arm away, but Adam hung on.

"Tell me! That fire's going to spread fast! You don't need any senseless deaths on your hands. You've got to know something."

The deputy twisted hard and broke free.

"In the subbasement." Then he was off and down the steps, running toward the blossoming red fires that threatened to engulf the nearest warehouses.

As Adam reached the open door, more explosions ripped through the manufacturing sector, spewing chunks of roofing and flaming tar paper into the sky. He grabbed the door frame and steadied himself, then plunged inside.

Dimmed gas lamps lit the foyer, hall and stairs. Seeing no obvious entrance to a lower level, Adam sped down the hall, testing each door. At the far end on the left, an open archway revealed a dimly lit stairwell heading down.

Leaping three and four steps at a time, Adam plunged around each corner until he saw a concrete landing and an open door. As he leapt to the landing, a redheaded female deputy came through the doorway, a large ring of keys in one hand.

Adam did not give her any time to recover from the shock of seeing him jump from the stairs and land directly in front of her. He wrenched the key ring from her hand.

"I'd suggest you hurry on and just look out for yourself. There's big trouble up there as you'll soon see."

The deputy sized up Adam and the angry, resolved look on his face, then turned and ran up the stairs.

Adam spun around and faced a narrow hall. Dimmed lamps cast faint light on the rounded edges of dull iron bars.

Holding cells!

"Hello, is someone there?" A woman's loud voice called anxiously. "We heard explosions! Please don't leave us here!"

Adam hurried down the hall to the first cell. It was Kate, Christine's friend, with her face pressed up close to the bars.

"Adam! What's going on?"

"We've got to out of here, fast!" Adam explained as he studied the keys.

"The round one," Lucius Morris said, stepping to Kate's side. He reached through the bars and pointed.

Adam did not waste time asking Kate and Lucius why they were here. He simply inserted the key Lucius had singled out and turned it.

The lock clicked. Adam jerked the door open.

"McDonald's men are taking Simon and New Eden down. I don't know what blew, but it was something really big. The manufacturing sector is ablaze all the way to the roofs. No time to waste!"

"They must've used the firebomb Simon was planning for Chicago," Kate offered, entering the hall, followed by Lucius. Simultaneously, they turned and faced Adam.

Confused, Adam reached out to push them toward the door, until he heard the noisy rattle of a cell door behind him.

With a wild and hopeful grin, Adam turned to the next cell. Joey smiled with cracked lips and exhausted eyes, his hands tightly gripping the bars.

"No time for a friend, huh?"

Adam worked the key, then threw the iron bars open with a loud clang.

Joey's knees buckled and he slumped forward into Adam's outstretched arms. Lucius and Kate quickly took Joey from Adam, supporting him on either side.

"Lucius and I will get Joey out," Kate said, her faced crumpled with concern. "Simon's got Christine. In his Grand Room—top floor."

Before Adam could react to the terrible news, Lucius grabbed his arm. Adam looked into Lucius' eyes and saw a great burden of shame and sadness. Lucius released the sleeve of Adam's jacket, his tortured face etched with distress.

Adam knew the haunted look all too well. Guilt was a terrible taskmaster, and integrity, once lost, seemed impossible to regain. Adam firmly clasped his hand on Lucius' shoulder.

"Take care of Kate and Joey. Who knows what those deputies will do if they spot the three of you. Make sure they get safely out of harm's way."

Something bright flickered in Lucius' eyes.

"With my life."

Simon stood at a window and watched as the growing blaze spread fiercely through the manufacturing sector and into the Brown and Tan sectors and the dining halls. Hundreds of families scampered away from the swarming red and orange flames that now leapt from buildings to trees and homes, fueled by self-induced updrafts.

"Impossible!" Simon screamed, grabbing a chair and slamming it halfway through the window. Shattering glass tinkled around his feet. Simon whipped around, his blood boiling and his entire body shaking from head to toe.

Gnashing his teeth, Simon suddenly knew that, somehow, Adam Vestry was the cause of this untimely disaster and the end of his greatest dream.

Quaking with fury, he stalked across the room, past Christine, to his desk and picked up his black satchel. His burning eyes glanced over at the now open and empty wall safe. An unexpected calm momentarily fell over him. He used his purple sleeve to wipe spittle from the corners of his mouth. At least he would leave with his treasured ebon jewel box, his gems and cash reserves—enough for him to start over again somewhere else, with a new name, a new identity and a new opportunity.

As Simon turned around, a dark crack suddenly appeared in the middle of the wall-length panorama. The crack and shadows widened until the door swung fully open.

Adam Vestry leapt into the room.

Adam's searching eyes found Christine's first, her face wet from crying, then darted to Simon where he stood at his desk, motionless, his hand resting on a small leather satchel.

"Adam!" Christine exclaimed, her voice hoarse.

Adam strode into the room and knelt by Christine's chair. With his pocketknife, he carefully cut through the ropes pinning Christine's arms and ankles to the chair. In moments, she was free.

He stood and reached to help Christine, but found himself staring down the barrel of a small pistol.

Simon now stood directly behind Christine. His rigid stance and his steady hand underscored the anger and deliberation in every slowly spoken syllable.

"Very heroic, Mr. Vestry. And very stupid. Did you truly think I wouldn't interfere?"

Simon's wild hair hung around his face and shoulders. His dark eyes, brimming with hatred, peered from behind long white strands.

He backed up two steps, well out of arm's reach from Adam. "Get her out of the chair. Now!"

Adam took Christine's shaking hands and pulled her to her feet, never taking his eyes off hers.

Christine knew from the look in Adam's gaze that he had forgiven her.

"Kate?" she whispered through tears.

Adam kept his eyes on hers and nodded ever so slightly, yes.

Christine felt the hard shove of a bony hand in the middle of her back, pitching her forward against Adam's chest.

"Shut up!" Simon bellowed, thrusting the pistol toward Christine. "And get moving!"

Christine did not hear Simon's last words.

She watched Adam's face flash bright orange as he froze wide-eyed with fright. Christine looked back.

Like a huge flaming kite, a tumbling section of burning roof and glowing shingles fell from the sky straight at them, crashing through the windows and wall at the end of the room. A wave of fire, red sparks and shattering glass swept across the thick carpet as the floor shook beneath their feet.

Christine fell backward, then felt Adam's strong hands grab her under the arms and drag her back to her feet. As she and Adam staggered toward the open door, she stole a glance over her shoulder.

Simon lay on his side, brushing embers from a smoking white pants leg, pistol on the floor less than a foot away. The entire wall behind him was ablaze, curtains, paintings and even the ceiling.

Christine stumbled into the hall and into cooler air, Adam's arm around her waist. As they reached the landing at the top of the stairs, Adam stopped and doubled over, coughing and trying to regain his breath.

Then Christine heard a loud click behind her.

"Stop right there."

Simon Friend slowly circled to Christine and Adam's left. A growing orange brightness and a furious crackling sound told Christine that the fire was quickly consuming Simon's once-grand Grand Room.

Simon walked with his back toward the landing rail and the stairs, the pistol aimed at Adam's chest.

"Not a single step farther." Simon snickered.

"It's your end of the line, so to speak. Coming out here, together, on that train from Paradise. Thought you could make something of your life, did you? Instead, you ruined my dreams. And now, you'll pay for it."

Christine leaned forward and mustered all the courage she could. "No, Simon, we didn't ruin your dreams—you did! You've cheated and manipulated people all your life. And your dreams? What did you build? Nothing but a city of lies!"

Simon laughed, long and hard as he lifted the pistol and began to squeeze the trigger.

But Simon never heard the feet on the steps to his right. He never saw the large hand stab out. But in a moment of unexpected shock, he felt a thick finger jam painfully against his, blocking the trigger, followed the agonizing wrench of the pistol being pried from his fingers.

Simon screamed and tried to hang on, but the leverage exerted by a big, scar-faced man stepping quickly to his side was too great. The man tossed the handgun over the rail where it fell and clattered on the foyer's wooden floor two stories below.

Simon Friend slowly backed up to the rail, clutching his black satchel to his chest, his eyes blazing and his chin held high amid his royal mane of white hair.

The former chief of security suddenly appeared, one foot on the steps, one on the landing. He motioned to Christine and Adam to hurry. With the fire's growing roar behind them, they followed Lucius quickly down the steps.

Christine kept her face pressed against Adam's shoulder, but still heard Simon's terrified scream as he plunged swiftly past them in a blur of white and purple and flailing arms to the foyer below.

At the bottom of the steps, they had to walk around the sprawled body of Deputy Harris, arms and legs spread wide with his neck bent at an unnatural angle.

Lucius paused and swallowed hard. He looked from Harris' body to Christine and Adam. "Mike's man got him, right when we came in. He was quick. No mercy."

Then they looked up. To their right, in the center of the foyer, lay Simon McGee. Flat on his back, his body lay motionless with his hand still gripping the black satchel pressed to his chest, his mouth open, his eyes dull and staring upward.

Christine looked away as they hurried past and out the door, down the circular steps and onto the cobblestone walk. Within minutes, weak-kneed and trembling from the cold, they passed through the main gates, now flung wide open to let the fleeing families escape.

To the left, Joey and Kate waited with blankets, their faces reflecting both firelight and uninhibited joy. Lucius, however, was suddenly nowhere to be seen.

Standing side by side, each with blankets wrapped tightly around them, they watched as the Main Administration building collapsed into a flaming pyre of bricks and wood, spiraling columns of red sparks and glowing orange rubble.

CHAPTER 22
SAN FRANCISCO

As the train continued to gain speed and ramble down the tracks away from Chicago, Christine quietly exhaled and the last lines of worry vanished from her face.

Adam chuckled from across the dining car table and lowered his newspaper. He smiled as Christine reached over the table and brushed back a small curl of hair from his forehead. His eyes followed the gold band on the ring finger of her left hand.

"What struck you so funny?" Joey asked, taking the empty seat next to Adam. Only a small scar near the corner of his right eye remained from his three days in the dark belly of New Eden.

Adam folded the paper and handed it to Joey. He pointed halfway down one column.

Joey peered up and grinned. "So, it looks like some of Ol' Mike's boys are in pretty big trouble. You're the one who leaked the information to the press, aren't you? And just two weeks after your big exposé on Friend, I mean McGee."

Christine frowned as she watched Adam sip his coffee.

"Now why would I go and do something as dangerous as leaking information connecting McDonald and McGee?" Adam replied nonchalantly.

Joey let his head loll from side to side as he broke a hard roll into two pieces. "Yeah, right. Like you can really fool us."

"Fool who about what?" asked Kate as she tucked her dress and slid into the empty seat next to Christine. Joey handed Kate the paper and pointed to where she should begin reading.

"Apparently, four of McDonald's men have been tied to the fire at New Eden. Somebody leaked their names to the newspaper."

Christine looked down at the paper in Kate's hands. The words "unidentified source" stuck out like a sore thumb.

"Bottom line? If I did leak those names," Adam said, pausing and keeping his eyes from Christine's, his voice growing suddenly serious, "I could never admit to it, now could I?"

For a moment, silence ruled. Crossing Mike McDonald was no joking matter.

Christine broke the hush. She reached over and placed her hand on top of Adam's, their rings touching.

"The weather in San Francisco stays pleasant all winter, I hear," Joey said, changing the topic, stuffing the bread into his mouth.

Kate nodded excitedly. "And it'll be good to start over, in a new place. I think I'm going to really enjoy teaching, this time."

"You can say that again," Joey said, swallowing his bread. His expression softened as he looked at Adam. "And all I can say is, well, thanks."

"Nothing to thank me for. You and I make a pretty dynamic duo. I can't imagine breaking us up when there's so much news to print in San Francisco. We'll do great. And we'll find a good church that we can all attend."

"Where you go, I'll follow," Joey chuckled. "But no security details or jail cells this time."

"And no uniforms or spying on other people," Kate added.

Christine nodded. "We ignored the warning signs. When something looks too good to be true, you've got to carefully check it out."

Adam squeezed Christine's fingers gently. "You were in a tough place. McGee took advantage of you, tried to make himself a father-figure. He was a deceiver of the worst kind."

Christine shook her head. "I won't blame Simon. I can't. That's not what the Bible teaches. We're responsible for the company we keep, the close friends we make, and whom we choose to follow. Each of us knows the pain of bad decisions."

Christine smiled and looked at Kate, then to Adam and Joey. "But we've all made some good decisions, too."

Adam nodded. "Amen."

Joey grinned. He lifted his glass of water. "To true friends."

Kate followed. "To a fresh start."

Christine and Adam raised their glasses together and brought them clinking lightly against the other two.

"To pasts already forgiven," Adam offered cheerfully.

Christine smiled, her words brimming with joy. "And futures to be shared!"

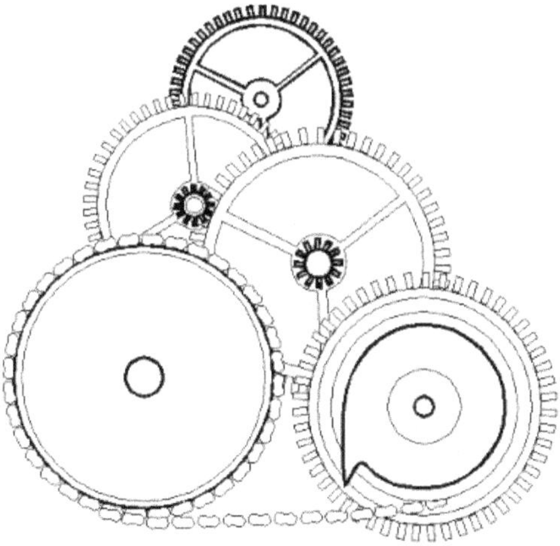

Check out the *Midas Touch* series...

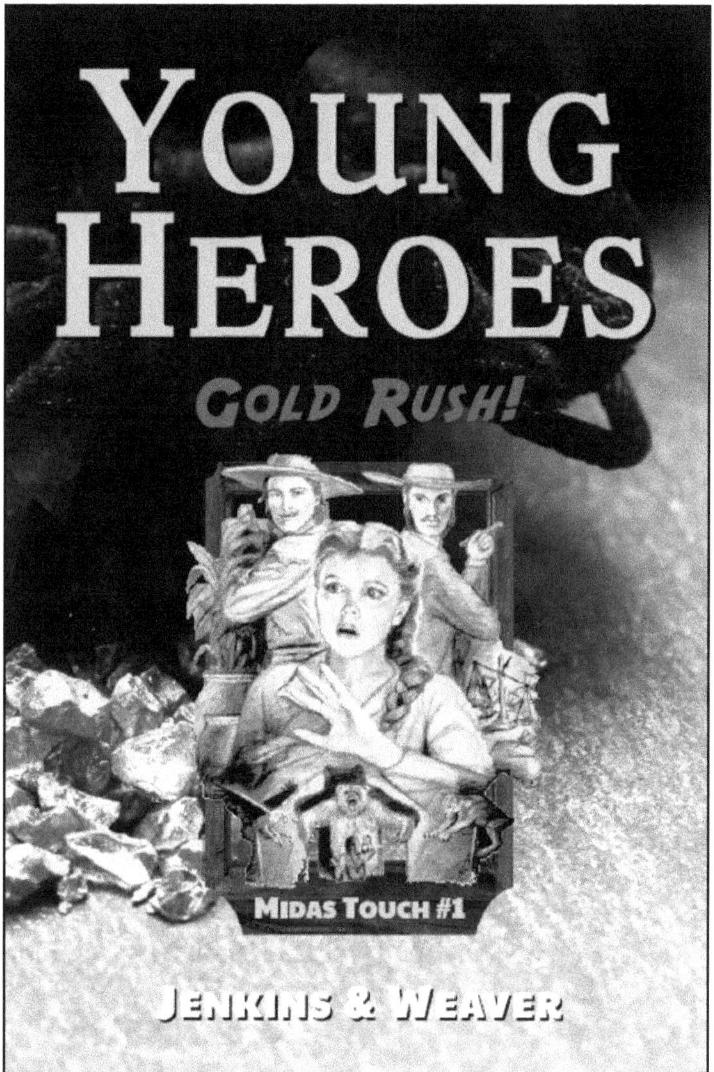

Book 1

"I want my sons and daughter to read
and be affected by this story."
Karen Adams, President,
Families in Support of Home Education"

CHAPTER 1

GOLD DIGGER

MARY leaned forward on her knees and tightly gripped her spade with both hands. She angled the blade toward the hard, bluish clay and gravel in front of her.

The sixteen-year-old ignored the stinging streams of sweat dripping from her auburn hair and dusty forehead into her wide-open brown eyes. She ignored the dark shadows of her two friends cast by the noonday sun.

Abruptly, the loud rattling sound filling the narrow ravine halted. She did not hesitate. She plunged the spade downward and pinned the snake to the ground behind its triangular head.

The snake wriggled once, then went limp. To be safe, Mary raised the spade and came down hard a second and a third time.

The two brothers whooped and laughed. Mary grabbed the dead snake with both hands and flung the two pieces into a clump of nearby brush.

"Last time that rattler's gonna mess with our diggin's!" exclaimed Tom Nielsson, who had just turned fifteen. He swung his shovel onto his shoulder.

Billy, a year younger, patted Mary on the back.

"Our diggings . . ." Mary muttered, wiping her hands on her torn corduroy pants.

They had panned the creek beds near the Feather River for

nearly a month. But for what? Hardly two ounces of gold—though they'd started mining the same week she and her missionary parents staggered into the town of Midas. Their journey from Shawnee Mission, Kansas, to northern California took three deadly months. Starting in March, they'd come west with an outfit of eighteen families who called themselves the Kansas Trading Company. They'd ridden and then walked a thousand miles over endless plains, perilous deserts and rugged mountains.

Mary didn't want to think about how many died from accidents, fever, and chills that spring. Of those who survived the journey, only her parents had chosen to live so far north of San Francisco.

She scrunched her sunburned face and blew a tickling wisp of hair away from her freckled nose. Digging and sifting the rocky soil—mining was hard! And when they panned the streambeds, the cold water numbed their fingers. Even on a hot summer day!

She sighed. As her shadow shifted, sunlight struck the blue clay and broken rock where her spade had severed the snake.

A yellow glint caught her eye. Mary drew in a sharp breath. Her heart skipped a beat. Could it really be?

"Tom! Billy! I've found color!"

She rubbed a dirty sleeve across her face to wipe the sweat, then pulled out her knife. Hunkering down, she scraped it along a narrow crevice in the rock. The brothers dropped to their knees and yanked off their hats to get a better look.

Carefully Mary lifted her knife from the crevice. Her mouth hung open, her eyes riveted on the knife and its glittering load.

Balanced on the level blade gleamed a dozen thick, bright flakes of gold.

"El Dorado, at last!" Billy yelled at the top of his lungs.

Mary watched both brothers joyously fling their tattered and dusty hats high into the air. She imagined the Spanish conquistadors would have tossed their shining helmets too, had they ever discovered that legendary city of gold.

"A real honest to goodness lode!" Tom exclaimed.

Mary yanked a leather pouch from her belt and pried it open with her fingers. Then she slowly tipped the knife. The chips of gold fell inside one by one.

They dug the clay-filled crevice most of the afternoon. More than once, they stopped to hoot and marvel. In three hours, they found more gold than many a seasoned miner found in two weeks.

Mary climbed to her feet and brushed the loose dirt from her pants. With a wide smile, she tossed the pouch from one hand to the other. "I'd say we'll split at least a pound, maybe more."

She handed Tom the pouch so he could feel the weight of success.

Tom just shook his head in disbelief, then tossed it to Billy.

"At sixteen dollars and ounce, that's eighty to ninety dollars for each of us," Mary figured out loud as she loosened her long braid of hair.

"What are you gonna do with your share, Mary?" Billy asked.

"I'm not sure," she said, picking up her canteen and pouring water over her upturned face. She shook the water from her thick hair. "This is my first bonanza."

"Ours too!" Tom said, snatching the pouch from Billy. "We've got to stake our claim. Mary, go ahead—you found the pile."

Billy grabbed their axe and handed it to Mary after she finished weaving her hair back into a braid that reached halfway down her back.

Taking the axe, Mary glanced around and found an old stump to the right side of the ravine. She walked over, swung the axe up over her head, and then slammed it down into the stump.

Billy pulled a sharpened piece of charcoal from his pocket and knelt by the stump. He spoke the words proudly as he wrote them on the handle of the axe.

"EL DORADO CLAIM!"

Tom dropped the pouch into Mary's waiting and open palm.

"July 28, 1849—a day we'll all remember," Mary beamed.

"Now, let's go record our claim and find out what our gold is really worth!"

Check out *Stories to Inspire*.

"I loved every book in this series."
Erin, homeschool mother of four

CHAPTER 1
UNDER A CLOUD

"**HEY**, boy! What's your name?"

"Bob Chester."

"Where are you going with that basket of groceries?"

"To deliver an order to one of my guardian's customers."

"Are you honest?"

"I hope so, sir," replied Bob, his face expressing surprise that his probity should be questioned.

The man who had hailed Bob Chester appeared to be about twenty-five years old, and his clothes were well-fitting, giving him the air of a man of means. With him were two other men, one of whom, several years older, was also well dressed. The third member of the group was entirely different from the others. His clothes were grotesque, and bore every trace of having been purchased in some country store. His derby hat was green-black, and apparently a size too small, judging from the manner in which it rested on his head. Had not his appearance bespoken that he was a stranger come from the country to see the sights of New York, his face, sunburned and honest, would have proclaimed him as one unaccustomed and unfamiliar with the wiles of a great city.

Prior to his having been addressed, the boy who had given his name as Bob Chester had noticed the difference between the three men as they stood in earnest conversation on the sidewalk, and instinctively he had been attracted by the frankness of the countryman's face. He had been wondering why the two New Yorkers were so interested in the other man, but the unexpectedness of his being accosted had driven all thought from his mind, and he had given his answers as though compelled by the searching glance the younger of the two men had directed at him.

All three watched him intently, and as he made his answer that he hoped he was honest, the elder of the New Yorkers exclaimed:

"I think he will do, Harry."

"Well, if you say so, all right," returned the other, and then turning to Bob, he asked:

"Would your guardian object seriously if you did not deliver your order for about half an hour?"

"I don't know. Saturday is always a busy day at the store, and Mr. Dardus always scolds me if I don't get right back. It doesn't make any difference to him how far I have to go, he always thinks I should be back within fifteen minutes after I have started. So I'd rather not delay—because I don't like to be scolded," added the boy, as though by way of apologizing for his refusal.

"Well, if we gave you a dollar, don't you think you could stand the old man's scolding, if you were half an hour late?" asked the elder of the New Yorkers, at the same time putting his hand in his pocket and drawing forth a large roll of bills, which he opened ostentatiously. The figures were so large that Bob's eyes seemed as though they would pop out of his head, so eagerly did they scan them. The man extracted a dollar bill.

The sight of so much money in the possession of one man fairly hypnotized the boy, and he replied:

"Do you mean you will give me a whole dollar if I will wait here half an hour?"

"That's what!" exclaimed the man with the roll of bills. "But there is a little more to it. Our friend, Mr. Anthony Simpkins, and we, have an important business transaction in hand, involving fifteen hundred dollars. My friend and I don't happen to have more than five hundred dollars with us, while Mr. Simpkins has seven hundred and fifty, and so we want you to hold this money while my friend and I go to our bank and get the two hundred and fifty dollars more, which is our share in the deal."

"What, me hold twelve hundred and fifty dollars!" exclaimed Bob, as though unable to believe his ears. "Why, you don't know anything about me. I might run off with it."

"You look honest," replied the man who had hailed him, "and that's why we stopped you. Besides, you wouldn't be able to run away if you wanted to, because Mr. Simpkins is going to wait here with you until we return."

"And you will give me a dollar just for keeping the money until you come back?" demanded Bob.

"Exactly."

"All right. That's half as much as I get for working a week."

"That's the boy. I am glad to see that you have the sense of thrift so strongly developed. Now we will just put Mr. Simpkins' seven hundred and fifty dollars and our five hundred dollars in this envelope, which you will keep until we return."

As he spoke, the elder of the New Yorkers counted out five hundred dollars, put it in the envelope, and then asked the countryman for his share. After verifying the amount, he placed it with the other money, then handed an envelope to Bob, exclaiming:

"Now you two stay right here, and we will be back within fifteen minutes."

"All right, sir," said Bob, as he grasped the envelope. And as his fingers closed about it, he unconsciously threw back his head, and squared his shoulders, proud of the thought that he had been selected as the custodian of such a large sum of money.

Again repeating their promise to return within a quarter of an hour, the two New Yorkers hastened away, and were soon lost among the people who thronged the thoroughfare.

Oblivious as the people who live in New York are to the presence of their fellowmen, the sight of the man so obviously from the country and the bright-eyed, alert boy, closely clasping the envelope in one hand, while at his feet rested the basket packed with groceries, attracted many a passing glance.

Between Simpkins and Bob, however, no words were exchanged, though each, while apparently gazing at the passersby, kept a sharp lookout upon the other.

Minute after minute went by, without the return of the two men, who had said they were going to the bank for money, and as the time wore on without their re-appearance, Simpkins exclaimed:

"I wonder what's keeping them? I don't want to stand here all day."

"And I can't," said Bob. "I will be more than half an hour late in getting back to the store, and I know Mr. Dardus will be very angry. I most wish I hadn't said I'd wait. It just shows that Mr. Dardus is right when he says there is no pleasure in having money that isn't earned honestly, and getting a dollar for just holding this money isn't really honest work."

"Well, if you think you ought to be delivering your groceries, why not give the envelope to me? I'll stay here and wait, though I must say I am getting tired."

"Oh, no," said Bob. "I gave my word that I would stay, and I will."

The countryman's suggestion that he be entrusted with the money aroused Bob's suspicion, for he remembered that the others had placed five hundred dollars in the envelope, and he thought it was a scheme on the part of Simpkins to get possession of this money. So that after this interchange of words, both lapsed into silence.

As the quarter hour lengthened into a half, then to three-quarters, and finally to an hour, without the re-appearance of the two well-dressed New Yorkers, Bob's dread of his guardian's anger outweighed his desire to earn the dollar, and he finally exclaimed:

"I can't wait any longer, honest I can't." And then, chancing to catch sight of a policeman standing on the corner about a hundred feet away, a way out of the difficulty suggested itself, and he said to the countryman:

"I tell you how we can fix it. We will go over to that policeman and explain the matter to him, and I'll ask him to hold the envelope until those men come back."

And without giving Simpkins time to protest, Bob picked up his basket, and led the way to where the guardian of the law was standing, indolently surveying the crowd.

Casting a contemptuous glance at the two ludicrous figures that approached him, the policeman first listened to the excited explanation of the boy indifferently, then with incredulity, and finally with amusement.

"I have heard of such easy marks, but I never expected to see them in flesh and blood," exclaimed the officer, when Bob stopped speaking. "So you think you are holding some money in that envelope, do you, kid? Well, I'll bet a year's pay that there is nothing in it but old paper."

And while the countryman and the boy gazed at him in speechless dismay, the policeman took the envelope from Bob's hand, opened it, and drew forth to their startled gaze a roll of tissue-paper.

"I told you so," grunted the policeman, but further comment was interrupted by the actions of Simpkins.

No sooner had he discovered that he had been swindled than he shouted at the top of his lungs:

"I've been robbed! I've been robbed! They've stolen seven hundred and fifty dollars from me!"

The loud, excited words and the gesticulations of the grotesquely-garbed man quickly drew the attention of the passersby, and in a trice the victims of the swindlers and the policeman were the center of a curious throng of people.

"I want my money! I want my money!" bellowed Simpkins.

"You stand a fine chance of getting it," returned the policeman, "but I will do what I can for you. I'll take you around to the police station, and you can make a complaint to the sergeant and give him a description of the 'con' men."

As word of the swindle was passed among the crowd, various were the comments and bits of advice offered.

At first Bob had been too stunned by the discovery that he had been made an innocent party to the swindle even to think, but as he gradually recovered from the unpleasant surprise, his one thought was to get away from Simpkins, to deliver his groceries and get back to the store as quickly as possible. In order to carry out this plan, he began to worm his way through the constantly increasing crowd.

One of the men who were offering advice chanced to see him, and cried:

"There goes the boy! He was probably standing in with the swindlers. Why don't you arrest him, Mr. Officer?"

"That's the thing to do," agreed several others, and the policeman, evidently thinking that it would be a wise procedure for him to seize someone in connection with the swindle, leaped after Bob, grasped him roughly by the shoulder, and started for the station-house, followed by Simpkins and those of the crowd who had nothing better to do.

Arrived at the police station, the countryman and the patrolman both talked at once, while Bob stood in silence, overcome by the disgrace of his arrest.

Taking his pencil, the sergeant stopped the countryman's torrent of words, and began to ask him questions as to his meeting with the strangers, eliciting the information that he had met them coming over on the ferry-boat from Jersey City, and that the business deal they had proposed was the betting of fifteen hundred dollars on a race horse that was sure to win.

"It's a pity there isn't a law to keep you country people out of the cities," grunted the sergeant, when the details of the story had been told him, and then, turning to the policeman, he said:

"You did right in bringing along the boy, McCarty. He is evidently one of the gang, or he wouldn't have been passing along the street just as he was. We may be able to learn from him who the 'con' men are, and where they hang out. Search him, and then take him back to a cell. I'll send a couple of plain-clothes men in to talk with him."

And grabbing Bob by the arm, the policeman dragged him toward the door which led to a cell.

YOUNG HEROES

ENJOYABLE FOR READERS OF ALL AGES

A TRAIL OF TEARS

CENTURY WAR # 1

DANIEL SWEETWATER is a 16-year-old Delaware Indian living with his preacher father among the Cherokee in 1838. They are forced to march with the Cherokee on a 1000-mile journey from Georgia to the Oklahoma Territory.

Cruel men and the daily pains of injustice hammer mercilessly at Daniel's faith in God. But God provides hope through a wise frontiersman and a missionary's courageous daughter. When unexpected tragedy comes, Daniel is faced with a choice. Will he follow a dark trail of vengeance? Or will he follow the light of truth and discover a special mercy hidden within his Christian heritage?

INVISIBLE EMPIRES

JOSIAH WASHINGTON, a 16-year-old former slave, longs to experience the true meaning of freedom in 1870's Philadelphia. Deeply hurt by the cruel injustices he has suffered, Josiah is unwittingly drawn into a convoluted plot to bring the Ku Klux Klan into the North.

When Josiah learns that he is but a small pawn in a much bigger and devious game, he must find a way to stop the KKK from igniting Philadelphia into a violent war of racial hatred.

Heroes and enemies spanning two generations collide, as God calls the past into account and brings evil men to justice.

CENTURY WAR # 2

INSPIRE THE HERO!

A CITY OF LIES

CENTURY WAR # 3

CHRISTINE THOMPSON and ADAM VESTRY are reunited four years following their first adventure in *The Invisible Empire.* The year is 1876. Chicago, five years after the Great Fire, continues to rebuild its reputation as Queen of the West.

Christine, wanting to make her own way, joins a utopian community called New Eden, where new ideas, hard work and equality promise a recreated Paradise. Adam, an investigative reporter, pursues connections between organized crime and business. Following a trail of corruption to the doorstep of New Eden, Adam must find a way to rescue Christine and foil the evil that seeks to bring flames and destruction to Chicago once again!

GOLD RUSH!

MIDAS TOUCH # 1

MARY MUHLENBERG is an ambitious 16-year-old who joins the California Gold Rush in 1849. But despite her missionary father's warnings, she exchanges her Bible for a spade.

Touched by gold fever, Mary makes an ill-advised alliance with conniving entrepreneurs from Midas, a nearby mining town. Her escapades will threaten her father's work among the local tribes, compromise her faith and family, and imperil not only her life, but the lives of her friends.

When Mary finds herself trapped and alone, she is confronted by her poor judgment. She must face the darkness within herself. Only then will she be ready for the greatest test of her life.

YOUNG HEROES

ENJOYABLE FOR READERS OF ALL AGES

WRECKERS OF THE REEFS

STORIES TO INSPIRE

KIDNAPPED at birth by an evil uncle in 1879, Lucas escapes to freedom with the help of a kindly captain of a merchant ship. The ship goes down leaving Lucas clinging to the shattered mast, the lone survivor.

A "surfman," Abner Peake of the U.S. Life Saving Service, brings Lucas into his home. Now, Lucas dreams of becoming a surfman, like those brave men who rescued him.

Lucas must risk everything he has gained in a life or death rescue mission with the surfmen, leading to a surprising and life-changing discovery.

PONY EXPRESS PURSUIT

EXCITED by his new position as a Pony Express rider, 16-year-old Jack Bailey of Rainbow Ridge, Colorado, has no idea of a coming danger that will fall upon him and his community. Jack is tasked with receiving and delivering a very important document – the deed to a motherlode gold mine. But others know the document's worth and await a chance to steal it.

When Jack is drugged and his mail is stolen, will he rise up and rally the community? Will Jack finally prove that he is a man worthy of the title Pony Express Rider?

STORIES TO INSPIRE

Inspire the Hero!

Newsboy Empire

ORPHANED, Jimmy Small works as a newsboy near New York City's infamous Five Points in the summer of 1907. Sleeping in a garbage-littered alley, Jimmy awakens to find a young amnesiac boy named Philip sleeping next to him. They become fast friends and form a business partnership.

Philip is kidnapped by young thugs who believe he is the son of wealthy parents. Will a quarter dollar and a promise be enough for Jimmy to save his friend and business partner? Will the mystery of Philip's identity and Jimmy's dream of owning a newsstand ever be fulfilled?

STORIES TO INSPIRE

Saved by the Wireless

STORIES TO INSPIRE

MYSTERIOUS messages haunt 16-year-old Tom Barnes as he works at his new telegraph station in the New England town of Rockley Cove in 1911. Nearly every day, the word "Donner" comes across the wire.

When the biggest storm of the season sweeps in along the coast, Tom picks up a distress signal from a passenger liner at sea—the Olivia. His friend Grace is aboard and Tom must act. He commandeers a hulking motorboat and sets out for the imperiled liner.

Amid the deadly, tossing waves, Tom's courage and resolve are tested and his hard-earned success hangs on every decision. Will they reach the Olivia in time? Can he find a way to save Grace and the others? Will he survive to solve the "Donner" mystery?

YOUNG HEROES

ENJOYABLE FOR READERS OF ALL AGES

TREACHERY ON THE GREAT LAKES

STORIES TO INSPIRE

ORPHANED in 1899 at the age of 14, apprentice longshoremen Nat Morton works on the Chicago docks but yearns to become a boat pilot. With a lost inheritance hanging over his head, Nat's lowly station in life provides him little hope.

A helpless figure flailing in the water creates an unexpected opportunity. Nat saves the *Jessie Drew*'s pilot and their friendship lands Nat behind the wheel in the pilot house.

A vicious storm with Nat at the wheel tests him to his core. Will he stay the course, save the ship, and the lives entrusted to him?

CALL OF THE PRAIRIE

BEHIND BARS in a New York City police station in 1904, 16-year-old Bob Chester ponders his bad luck. A menacing legal guardian and scheming con artists fuel Bob's dream of going west and becoming a cowboy. Released unexpectedly, he gathers the few dollars he has saved and flees New York for Oklahoma.

Working hard to prove himself as a ranch hand, Bob discovers a ruthless plot to steal his boss's property and holdings. Bob's character and wits will be tested to the utmost in a desperate race across the prairie to expose the plot and save his boss and new friend.

STORIES TO INSPIRE

INSPIRE THE HERO!

TRIAL BY FIRE

DISTRESSED by the failure of his town's bucket brigade to safely extinguish the fires plaguing Lakeville, 16-year-old high school student Jake Walters and his schoolmates create a volunteer fire company. It's 1903 and, during their summer vacation, the boys raise their own funds and purchase a used, water and hose pump wagon.

But a prominent citizen resists Jake's efforts, insisting that their bucket brigade is sufficient. When the town's biggest factory goes up in flames and a young girl is trapped inside the building, Jake must decide if he will risk his life and everything he has worked for when no one else steps up to rescue the girl.

STORIES TO INSPIRE

RACE FOR THE SKIES

STORIES TO INSPIRE

STRUGGLING to make his way, 15-year old Andy Nelson is a gifted mechanic in a 1910 Midwest town. He finds a customer's wallet, but his greedy boss, Seth Talbot, wants the money. Andy refuses, hoping to return the money to the customer. He banks the money and hides the empty wallet. This act defines the course of Andy's life and he is forced to flee the town

During his journeys, Andy helps an entrepreneur dislodge his biplane from a barn roof, striking up a friendship and a new job. When Andy learns to fly, he is entered in a great air race. But his past sneaks up on him when the greedy Talbot tracks him down to destroy his reputation and life.

Caught in a doubly dangerous race for the skies and the pursuit of justice, Andy's integrity and courage will be tried and tested as never before.

Young Heroes

More Great Stories

Ghost Pirates

TOM JEFFERSON MYSTERIES

WHEN a ghostly Blackbeard and his crew rise from the dead and begin haunting the people of Williamsburg, Virginia, young Tom Jefferson and his closest friend Will Blair set about to unravel the mystery.

Little do they realize the chain of events their bold actions will set into motion, events that will forever shape their lives, and the life of a fledgling nation.

This first book in the *Tom Jefferson Mystery* series gives readers a fresh and exciting look at one of America's storied characters and times.

Readers of all ages will enjoy this first book in the *Tom Jefferson Mystery* series.

I Love Baseball

SUMMER OF 1869 — the bustling riverfront city of Cincinnati, Ohio. Steamboats churn the Ohio River as the nation's ever-expanding economy thrives in the wake of the Civil War. Two 16-year-olds, Charlie Martin and his best friend Luther Robinson, love "base ball" and follow the exploits of America's first professional base ball team — the undefeated Cincinnati Red Stockings.

When a ruthless shipping magnate ends their dream for a Cincinnati Youth Club ball field, the two square off against one of Cincinnati's most powerful men, risking their honor, friendships and freedom to right a grievous wrong. Readers of all ages will enjoy this first book in the *Batter Up!* series.

BATTER UP! #1